PRAISE FOR MANUFAC

"It is all about people. Joe Sprangel's *Humanist Manufacturing: A Humanitarian Approach to Excellence in High-Impact Plant Operations* comes at the perfect time when our labor markets are in such flux because people are looking for valuable work, not just a paycheck. He gives us a turn-by-turn guide on how to infuse integrity and respect into your leadership style, your product design and your manufacturing strategy. Joe explains exactly how you can "do well by doing good." Along this journey, Joe shows how teams can build relationships and develop a sense of purpose to become not only better employees…..and better people."

—Christina Cain, Program Manager, Virginia Division of Economic Development and Community Vitality

"Filled with compelling examples of success and countless resources, the Humanist Manufacturing framework provides leaders with a step by step plan to a sustainable future."

—Jair Drooger, Co-Founder/Founder, CT Assist, The WellMent Company (Certified B Corporation), & MSL Consulting

"This is a welcome addition to the literature on Humanistic Business Management. How we conduct business and why we conduct business are all explored. The case studies of companies operating in a Humanist way are extremely helpful and enlightening. Humanism is not just a theoretical idea. It's a practical one that yields profitable results for the companies who apply it to their businesses. If you want to learn what it looks like to operate a manufacturing company in a Humanist way, Joe Sprangel's book is a must read."

—Jennifer Hancock, Founder, Humanist Learning Systems

"This book is a comprehensive approach to leading with the heart in a world full of hard nosed decision making. It ties together the many parts of modern management theory with the oft overlooked special circumstances of leadership in todays pressure cooker manufacturing environment. It is designed to be a helpmate, not a read through once and forget it book. With questions for reflection and additional readings relevant to each chapter it is designed to be on your desk as opposed to on your shelf. It is full of actionable ideas that can be applied both every day and during times of strategic thinking and planning. A great book from which any leader can learn!"

—Fred Keller, Founder and Chair, Cascade Engineering,
A Certified B Corporation

"Impact Makers is a Certified B Corp and an all-profits-to-charity model which allows us to provide maximum value to our clients while also supporting our community. As a socially-oriented business, we attract high-caliber personnel who have helped us contribute over $4 million in pro-bono consulting and cash support to our community partners since our founding almost 16 years ago. Manufacturing companies that follow Joe Sprangel's recommendation of adopting the B Corp model within his humanist manufacturing framework can also draw great people with a sense of purpose. Furthermore, organizations that use this business framework can become integral partners making a similar positive impact in their communities."

—Michael Pirron, Founder & CEO, Impact Makers

"Humanist Manufacturing is more than just a guide to follow. It gives us a good dose of the application of humanism in the book's arrangement. Dr. Sprangel views the reader as a seeker of knowledge and a believer that using humanism has better results for internal and external stakeholders and for leading people. I think my favorite parts are the questions he raises in the chapters which make you think and Closing Comments which tells the reader what he thinks. He certainly doesn't demand we take his view on faith. It is refreshing, however, to view all levels of employees as good, wanting to do good and innately capable of it instead of having to "manage" them so that they will perform. I think you will feel better reading this, even if you are not ready to apply Dr. Sprangel's 6 Phase Framework of Humanist Manufacturing. I did. It's not just for manufacturers, either. Most of my clients are service businesses and I will be sharing Dr. Sprangel's ideas with them — I already have in presentations he has made for me for my monthly online business forum."

—Jan Triplett, Ph.D. CBTAC, CEO, Business Success Center

"Academics can often fall into the trap of giving lip service to the value that practitioners can add to their fields. And, practitioners are often skeptical of the value academics can offer to the people who actually do the work. Joe Sprangel has managed successfully to bridge the gap and provide scholars and practitioners with valuable information that will help everyone during these tumultuous times to better understand the theory and the practice of manufacturing. By using the principles of humanism and applying them to the science of manufacturing, Joe has created a framework that helps professionals who are currently working in manufacturing, employees who are starting out, as well as students who are looking to better understand what manufacturing can be when the components of the manufacturing system are optimized. *Humanist Manufacturing: A Humanitarian Approach to Excellence in High-Impact Plant Operations* deserves a place on your bookshelf - but only after you actually read the material and work through the Chapter Reflection Questions. It is practical scholarship at its best."

—Joanne Tritsch, Ph.D, MBA Director & Assistant Professor,
Mary Baldwin University

HUMANIST MANUFACTURING

HUMANIST MANUFACTURING

A HUMANITARIAN APPROACH TO EXCELLENCE IN HIGH-IMPACT PLANT OPERATIONS

DR. JOE SPRANGEL

EMMANUEL STRATEGIC SUSTAINABILITY

ISBN: 979-8-218-08993-1 (paperback)
ISBN: 979-8-218-08994-8 (e-book)

Library of Congress Control Number: 2022920033

Edited by Arlynda Boyer
Proofread by Linda Reviea
Cover design by Standout Arts, LLC
Interior design by Jenny Lisk

Published by Emmanuel Strategic Sustainability, Staunton, Virginia, USA

With hope for a better world for my granddaughters,
Cloey, Emma, McKenna, and Noelle,
who inspired me to write this book

CONTENTS

FOREWORD

DR. JACKIE STAVROS

In the Introduction, the author, Joe Sprangel, asks you to reflect on the question, "can manufacturing be more than a production operation?

Imagine your operation being more than a production facility. Our organizations are made of people and those people are the driving force of your production. In this book, Joe presents a *humanistic manufacturing framework* that aligns with how your employees can be more than just line and staff people. This book can help you develop strategic and operational excellence practices that can impact your people's performance and commitment, which in turn impacts productivity in a positive way. The outcomes go beyond profit to creating workplaces that can work for all. He presents dozens of organizations doing this and doing it very well! These are organizations who are *human-centered* focus and are thriving because of it.

This book aligns with my humanistic AI approach to organization life; no, we are not talking about Artificial Intelligence, it is Appreciative Inquiry. Appreciative Inquiry (AI) is one of the most effective and widely used approaches for fostering positive change. AI has earned national and international recognition for creating a positive revolution in change with global brands like Apple, Boeing Corporation, Coca-Cola, Green Mountain Coffee Roasters, Interface Carpets, Ben and

Jerry's Ice Cream, British Airways, United Nations, VISA, Proctor & Gamble, and Vitamix just to name a few. A defining factor in the accomplishments of these organizations is their focus on building from *strengths* – what is working well, what is life-giving, what is possible, *opportunities*, what do your stakeholders care deeply about, *aspirations*, and how do you know you are making a positive differences, *results*. Learning to SOAR by asking a generative question: how might we move forward together in a sustainable way that considers the whole system?

While the theory and practice of AI and SOAR or the call to bring humanism into your organizations are not new (yet might be new to some reading this book), this book, *Humanistic Manufacturing: A Humanitarian Approach to Excellence in High-Impact Plant Operations*, is a new and worthwhile read because it blends many theories, practices, assessments, and tools with evidence-based research in a thoughtful and responsible way. Joe has brilliantly assembled a framework with a sequence of phases and proven practices that address the triple bottom line that is *doing well by doing good* not only for the organization but to your people and our planet with purpose and passion. The six phases get to knowing and understanding *what* to do, *why* to do it, and *how* to do it:

- Phase 1: Humanist Commitments – how to build commitment
- Phase 2: Leadership Development – how to motivate and model the way
- Phase 3: Develop Internal Operations – how to create operational excellence
- Phase 4: Employee Centric – how to develop your employees to their fullest potential
- Phase 5: Positive External Impact – how to support all your stakeholders and eco-system
- Phase 6: Strategic Planning – how to facilitate a whole system strategic plan and lead change

Joe seamlessly blends his down-to-earth, heart-giving personality and unique background (30 years of manufacturing experience with 15 years of sustainable practices) to offer readers first-hand insights and experiences into the importance of knowing thyself before leading others as well as knowing your executive team and how to align values, vision, mission, and purpose to organization goals and objectives that will produce results. He explains how to build a sustainable operating production system that can achieve operational excellence in product design, material selection, processes, and control systems that support both employee well-being and our environment. Each chapter dives into how to make it part of your organization's life. I love practical books and appreciate that each chapter starts with a quote to deepen your thinking and clearly lays out what you will learn and why and ends with reflection questions, checklists, and resources upon which you can act. You can build an amazing library just based on Joe's reading suggestions!

What stood out for me the moment I picked up this book was the word "human". That is to both invest in humankind and to be a kind human. Joe does both very well. The book is filled with a treasure trove of stories and resources. I love the *Ten Commitments of Living Humanist Values* in Chapter 1 and how this book starts and ends with the iconic Ray Anderson, founder and former CEO of Interface Carpets. I met Ray at the 2004 Business as an Agent of World Benefit – Sustainability Conference at Case Western Reserve University in Cleveland, OH. He read the poem by Glenn C. Thomas (1996) – *Tomorrow's Child*. This poem can be found in the last chapter of this book. In these pages, it is wonderful to see how Ray's journey has ignited both of our sustainability epiphanies and impacted our journeys (that was a special treat to read).

Joe truly models the way with all the learnings in this book. He has a wealth of knowledge and experience, which should be expected of any author who writes a reputable book, and he also writes with such inspiration, humility, and doses of humor to ground you. I admire Joe's curious nature, and all the questions he asks us to consider! He certainly walks the talk of *Humanistic Manufacturing* in how he lives his life and works with others. Thank you, Joe, for sharing your "North Star" with us in the book to support those in a manufacturing environment what is possible. My career started in a software manufacturing environment, and I see the value of this book to those organizations who want to have a more humanistic approach to best serve its stakeholders – your advice is enduring.

To the readers, I expect that you will want to reference this book many times because creating an exemplary manufacturing operation that puts your employees at the core of your operations is a neverending journey of learning, being, and doing. The *Humanist Manufacturing Framework* can build the DNA of your operations. I believe that most know we should do what Joe is advocating, and the value of this book is *what* do we do and how do we do it.

I love that you share the story of how your training for and completing of the Ironman Competition coincided with you becoming a humanistic manufacturer! For those who want to learn a bit more about Joe before starting the book, just jump to the last chapter first – it is my favorite chapter. Make sure you read the Preface because it gives Joe's why and why this book is a gift to each of you. Thank you, Joe, for this very special book and for modelling the way!

Jacqueline (Jackie) Stavros
Professor, College of Business and IT
Lawrence Technological University
Southfield, Michigan, USA
jstavros@ltu.edu

PREFACE

An interview session for a plant manager position I was pursuing was with their VP of Accounting & Finance. Toward the end of our time together, he commented, "You are not like others here at our company." The tone of his voice made me feel that he saw this as a favorable characteristic. I eventually ended up with the job and did learn that I was indeed unlike most others working for that organization.

The reality was that his comment was nothing new to me. I have worked for nine different employers over 27 years for various reasons. One as short a tenure of eight months and none longer than five years. Four employers asked me to leave because they were "going in a different direction." In one case, their customer wanted to hire me when I was let go because they respected what I stood for, and I would have been their key liaison to my former employer. In a second instance, the parent company management fired the person who let me go and asked that I return because they recognized that I was of value to the company. A common theme was that I was not a good fit for organizations despite being a productive employee. I was looking for something more than the traditional approach to manufacturing.

Ultimately, I tell people I had a mid-life crisis and decided to become an academic. While it was during my mid-life, it was far from a problem. I had long felt a call to teach as far back as my teens, and something triggered in me that it was time to follow that path. I began that transition when I was with my last manufacturing employer. After researching various teaching options, I decided to go the professor route at the higher education level. To do so meant earning a doctorate, gaining teaching experience, and getting published in academic journals. In three years, I transitioned to academia, taking my first full-time teaching job in Fall 2007.

Three things changed for me during this career transition and have been essential in defining my current being. The first was a documentary shown in a doctoral session taught by Dr. Jackie Stavros. The video was about Interface, which highlighted the leadership of Ray Anderson, an industry sustainability pioneer. Dr. Stavros also impacted me in a second way by introducing me to Appreciative Inquiry and the SOAR framework used for strategic planning. The third was being introduced to the B Corporation movement by Christina Cain. Their "Doing Well While Doing Good" approach to generating profit but integrating an environmental or social purpose enthralled me. The B Impact Assessment immediately resonated with me as it is a highly organized and expansive approach to guiding an organization to becoming a responsible business operation.

As I viewed the documentary on Ray Anderson, then the founder and chairman of Interface, one of his statements hit home. He shared the details of his "spear in the chest epiphany" after reading *The Ecology of Commerce: A Declaration of Sustainability*[1] by Paul Hawken. Anderson's move to shape Interface's business practices through a sustainability lens ignited a purpose in my life to use business as a force for good. The Ray Anderson ministry of sustainable business became my North Star to support the development of industry leaders.

Thankfully Dr. Stavros entered my life when they accepted me into the Doctor of Business Administration program at Lawrence Technological University in Southfield, MI. When she introduced me to Appreciative Inquiry, which draws from positive psychology, my initial reaction was that it was a bit "touchy-feely." I remember her telling me that this was a reaction she usually received from engineering types.

As my coursework progressed, she later introduced her SOAR framework for strategic planning. SOAR (Strengths, Opportunities, Aspirations, and Results) focuses on institutional strengths. It is a shift from the more traditional SWOT analysis where weaknesses and threats are reframed as Opportunities. SOAR uses a positive lens to understand the whole system by including all relevant stakeholders as internal and external voices of the organization. A simple change in perspective that I have found leads to a deeper level of stakeholder engagement and buy-in. In later chapters, we will use SOAR as a strategic planning approach for the organization.

In exploring the B Corporation movement, I learned of Fred Keller. Keller founded Cascade Engineering Inc[2] in 1973 with six employees molding plastic parts. The company now has 15 plants in six US locations and an operation in Budapest, Hungary, with 1,600 employees. These results would be enough success for many, but Keller felt the need to make a positive difference by doing business using a triple bottom line (TBL) of people, planet, and profit. As a result, Cascade Engineering joined a growing list of Certified B Corporations,[3] now at more than 5,000 companies, in 2010. In addition, they connected with others committed to holding their business to a high standard of verified environmental and social performance, legal accountability, and public transparency.

An element of faculty work in higher education is conducting research and publishing the results. My focus is on sustainability, strategic planning, and change management. As I dove deeper into this work, very troubling knowledge became known as I did the literature reviews on these topics. A few examples of the most pressing issues are:

- Too much human suffering - Too many people around the globe are currently unable to meet their basic human needs. In addition, there is a significant financial strain on 3.3 billion people – or forty percent – of the global population living on $5.50 or less per day (per the World Bank Group[4] in October of 2020).

- A stressed environment - Earth Overshoot Day[5] is an organization that calculates the day each year when the global demand exceeds the available ecological resources and services. For example, the date for 2021 was July 29th. The detrimental impact exhibits a gross imbalance of supply and demand that is unsustainable long-term. The poor are the most harmed as climate change affects them as global temperatures rise, leading to changes in weather patterns, higher sea levels, and ocean acidification.[6]
- An employment gap crisis - In addition to these issues, the manufacturing industry faces many challenges. For example, a recent report[7] projects that 2.1 million jobs will go unfilled by 2030, a potential negative impact of one trillion dollars that year alone. Moreover, the current case will become even more pressing with the expected retirement[8] of 2.6 million baby boomers in the coming decade.
- Employee disengagement - One of the Gallup *State of the American Workforce*[9] report findings was that employee engagement is at 33% in the United States, startlingly low compared to the 70% result for the world's best companies. In the US, 16% of employees are actively disengaged. With only 33% engaged, that leaves 51% of the workforce in a state of just being present.

These and other challenges are real and just a few of many more. However, I began to see solutions to these issues that can create opportunities for groups that have been largely unseen or acknowledged as legitimate actors to date. Thus, I felt that an opportunity exists to create a more desirable vision of an approach to doing business that can help reduce the current harm to our world and its citizens.

Until a few years ago, I had a "nose to the grindstone" approach to my career. My misguided thought was that employers would notice if you worked hard and produced favorable results. Unfortunately, what happened was that I lost skin off my nose and the occasional job. On the other hand, others had successes I could achieve if I changed my point of view. During this timeframe, I became aware of a Recognized

Expert™[10] course offered by Dorie Clark. One outcome of the study was to develop our "breakthrough idea."

After a few iterations of my breakthrough idea, I decided to leverage my manufacturing industry and academic experience to become a recognized expert in responsible manufacturing. I would begin consulting, coaching, training/reskilling, and thought leadership around the reinvention of manufacturing, improving the previously shared environmental and social issues. Elements of becoming a recognized expert include thought leadership through the authorship of blog posts, articles, and books to inspire readers to take action. The hope is that it will lead to speaking engagements and consulting work where clients seek you out instead of chasing after work.

During this time frame, I became aware of Bob Chapman, the CEO of Barry-Wehmiller[11] and co-author of *Everybody Matters: The Extraordinary Power of Caring for Your PEOPLE Like FAMILY*.[12] Chapman was recently honored by Inc.[13] magazine as the #3 global leader of "visionary leaders who walk the talk of servant leadership." He has leveraged a culture of authenticity, collaboration, community, and trust to create high employee engagement and low turnover. As he reflected on his undergraduate accounting degree and MBA program, he realized that his business education focused on using people to leverage financial success and not on how his chosen leadership style would impact the lives of those employed by the company. The result of his epiphany led to the development of Truly Human Leadership.

The word "Human" stood out for me from Chapman's leadership approach. Building on my experience in the manufacturing sector, my research, and the success of those like Ray Anderson, Fred Keller, and Bob Chapman, we are missing a golden opportunity to maximize the human potential that can elevate manufacturing as an agent of positive global change. Done collectively in this industry, each community, region, and collectively the world can be a better place for all.

It would be naive to think that one book can provide everything one would need to transform an individual company, let alone an industry. There is no illusion of doing so with this one. Instead, the intent is to tie it all together in a meaningful way to guide company owners and leaders toward having a more impactful future. The goal was to share a massive body of work done by many others in a format that shows a logical series of steps. However, it is not an all-or-nothing proposition. Individuals can determine which elements from the book are essential to improving their company and integrate them into their operations.

I hope you enjoy reading the book and gain insight and drive to become a more responsible manufacturing leader.

Warm regards,
Joe

INTRODUCTION
MAXIMIZING HUMAN POTENTIAL IN THE MANUFACTURING SECTOR

"The big challenge is to become all that you have the possibility of becoming. You cannot believe what it does to the human spirit to maximize your human potential and stretch yourself to the limit."

—JIM ROHN, ENTREPRENEUR, AUTHOR, AND MOTIVATIONAL SPEAKER

You wake up in the morning, and as you wipe the sleep from your eyes, a wide grin spreads across your face. The excitement wells up inside you as it is another workday in the manufacturing industry. But do you think I cannot possibly look forward to going into the plant today? If so, you are likely in an unfulfilling job and not able to move toward reaching your full potential as a human. Rather, imagine how much more enthusiasm you would feel if your work led you on a path toward Maslow's level of self-actualization or the ultimate one of transcendence.[1] You then begin to collaborate to create individual and household thriving for those in your community. Additionally, other global plant operations have a similar impact on improving the world for every citizen.

But wait, the expectation is to do this in a manufacturing environment? That is not what we do. We produce things for consumption by others. The work is repetitive, dirty, hot in the summer, cold in the winter, and long hours. We focus on production rates, quality issues, product and process design, customer sales, and the struggle to find new employees to work in an industry seen as increasingly undesirable by younger generations. We do not have time to worry about our employees reaching their full potential, let alone worry about our community or spending time thinking about improving the world. It is not just us; no one else in our industry has time to do this either.

The likely reality is that you are reading this book because you are looking to do something different. You may be the next generation of company owners wanting to take a different approach than the family members who have entrusted you to carry on the business. Are you a CEO who leads a company that cannot find enough qualified people to fill all open positions? Is there pressure from customers or investors to improve the bottom line? Maybe you aspire to become a future leader or head up your own manufacturing operation. On the other hand, you may be part of an organization well along the path toward becoming a highly human-centered business, just beginning the process, or somewhere between. Ultimately, if you desire to use manufacturing as a force for good, you will benefit from reading this book. Additionally, there is growing evidence that doing the right things from an environmental and social impact leads to better financial performance.[2]

Imagine working for a company that values all humans impacted by their manufacturing operation. Employees not only make a living wage but have the opportunity to maximize their full potential in a work environment that motivates them. Their well-being is essential to their employer, providing a safe work environment free of potential physical or mental harm. Suppliers are treated as valued partners. The organization has a solid commitment to diversity, equity, and inclusion that welcomes all genders, races, and ethnicities. They create opportunities for persons with perceived disabilities, individuals on the autism spectrum, returning citizens, veterans, women, and those needing support in breaking out of the poverty cycle. These are examples of integral initiatives to the human-centered approach to manufacturing.

But really, can manufacturing be something more than a production operation? You may not answer yes yet, but I hope to convince you otherwise before the end of this book. The content will begin with introducing a humanist manufacturing framework and the associated humanist commitments. Next, the importance of self-assessment and growth of the leadership team and the development of the "why," vision, mission, and values are the foundation for balancing the work to transition the company from the status quo to a more sustainable manufacturing operation. Achieving the mission requires a solid business operating system with well-designed approaches, deployment, continuous improvement, and integration to track the results' levels, trends, and industry comparisons. Then, it is necessary to explore human impact through product design, materials selection, manufacturing processes, and stakeholder maximization.

All of this work puts the workforce in the best position to impact the various stakeholders they support as the organization's frontline. Next, I offer several initiatives that can reduce current issues faced by manufacturing operations that significantly benefit a more comprehensive number of the community members in our neighborhoods. Finally, the focus shifts to developing strategic, tactical, and change management plans. While this may seem to be an improbable objective, there are manufacturing executives that have succeeded in moving from their former status quo to higher levels of success through a human-centered focus. Whether the aim is environmental or social, the ultimate benefit is a better world for all humans.

A SHORT LIST OF MANUFACTURING EXEMPLARS

Indeed, the manufacturing industry can be far more beneficial than the status quo to the world. Several manufacturing exemplars have laid the foundation for others to adopt or take to the next level. A few examples include:

· · ·

Ray Anderson, Interface. Anderson's move to shape Interface's business practices through a sustainability lens ignited a purpose in my life to use business as a force for good. He began his transition back in 1994, with the current result of Interface achieving zero impact[3] with a new challenge to become a regenerative organization.[4] Anderson's leadership led to a company where "doing well by doing good" led to survival during economic downturns and increased profitability driven by employees motivated by a higher purpose and goodwill in the marketplace.[5]

> "I used to think that my job didn't have anything to do with the environment. Then I realized that my job, as well as everyone else's job, impacts the environment in some way. And now advocating for sustainability has become my No. 1 responsibility."

Mary Barra, General Motors. Barra took over a toxic culture with significant challenges. However, our focus will be on her work to transform GM into a company that creates "a world with zero crashes, zero emissions, and zero congestion."[6] Barra sees the need for significant adoption of sustainability implementation in the automotive industry. In a conversation with Dane Parker, the initial Chief Sustainability Officer for GM, Barra and Parker discussed their plan to engage all company team members by helping each impact the objective of zero emissions. The work will include a transition of production to electric vehicles (EVs), a circular economy, and manufacturing operations that all leave a zero footprint.

> "General Motors is joining governments and companies around the globe working to establish a safer, greener, and better world. We encourage others to follow suit and make a significant impact on our industry and on the economy as a whole."

Bob Chapman, Barry-Wehmiller. In 1975, Chapman was suddenly thrust into leading a bottle-washing business on the edge of bankruptcy. The epiphany of adding the human element came in the early 2000s. The work began earnestly to "move from a me-centric culture to a we-centric culture." He has leveraged a culture of authenticity, collaboration, community, and trust to create high employee engagement and low turnover. The succeeding twenty years have led to meaningful results. Chapman has taken a nearly bankrupt company and grown it to a $2 billion global business by acquiring 80 companies at 100 locations with 11,000 team members.[7]

> "Business could be the most powerful force for good in the world, if leaders would embrace the awesome responsibility of leadership. Caring for people and giving them meaning, purpose and fulfillment through their work is not in disharmony with creating value."

Yvon Chouinard, Patagonia. The company has a significant focus on running its organization through the lens of sustainability.[8] Their programs for materials, environment, and animal welfare responsibility are robust. The company has fair, humane, legal, and safe working conditions. There is also a fully transparent sharing of information regarding internal company operations and those across their supply chain. Chouinard's quote stated that he has always made money when making the best decisions for the planet. He echoes similar results focusing on creating a positive social and environmental impact, ultimately becoming more profitable.

> "I know it sounds crazy, but every time I have made a decision that is best for the planet, I have made money."

Virginie Helias, Proctor & Gamble. Helias' goal as Chief Sustainability Officer is a single mission[9] to embed sustainability into

P&G's brand building, business practices, culture, and innovation. P&G has the ambition to put a sustainable world in the hands of its consumers by building sustainable consumption[10] at scale. They look to delight the five billion purchasers of the global brands they produce. At the same time, they look to resolve the environmental concerns of climate change, resource scarcity, water insecurity, and waste.

> "Sustainability used to be a separate department, but now it's everyone's job. In our annual Employee Survey, 83% of our employees reported that they are contributing to the organization's sustainability efforts – that's 9 points up from two years ago."

Henrik Henriksson, H2 Green Steel. His leadership performance as an active leader in sustainability has resulted in his recent appointment as the CEO of H2 Green Steel (H2GS).[11] He accepted the responsibility to continue his previous work at Scania to provide products and services that offered profitable solutions for their customers while continuing the goal of becoming a leader in sustainable transport. H2 Green Steel will be a fossil-free large-scale steel producer with plans to produce 5 million tons of CO_2-free steel. The power source for this production facility will be an integrated Giga green hydrogen plant.

> "We have a strong team with a desire to deliver real impact, and I see great potential for us to accelerate the green industrial transition of both Sweden and Europe."

Fred Keller, Cascade Engineering. Keller focused on building a company that valued a "people, planet, and profit" approach. They are not interested in reaching organizational goals at the expense of their people. There is an understanding of living on the one earth available to us and building a sustainable approach to a business committed to reducing resources. By doing a better job of maximizing the potential of people and minimizing raw materials, the company generates greater profits that create increased positive benefits for all stakeholders. Cultivating a Triple Bottom Line culture has been beneficial to doing business.[12]

> "I believe that business, I mean really business, has this wonderful opportunity to change the world for the better. Not because we must, but simply because we can. But it will take a different mindset for the leaders than is mainstream today. Not because today's leaders are bad, but because the world's future needs are so much different from where we've been."

These are just a few of the many exemplars doing their work in the manufacturing sector responsibly and benefiting a wide variety of human stakeholders.

BARRIERS TO OTHER PLANT OPERATIONS ADOPTING A HUMAN-CENTERED FOCUS

My deepening knowledge of the experiences of organizations that have successfully integrated a human-centered focus into their operations is that they are making a significant positive environmental and social impact. Still, they also realize improved financial results, with many seeing substantial improvement. So why are more manufacturing operations not implementing similar sustainability initiatives if this is true?

My experience leads me to believe that the answer to the question is multifaceted and includes:

- Shareholder pressure to meet short-term results with minor or no accounting for long-term effects.
- Organizations are led by leaders who believe they are running their companies to current best business practices.

- Many companies are constantly fighting fires. As they fight one fire, others emerge. The focus would transition to the hottest fire while the embers of other issues continue to burn, only to reignite later.
- Large customers expect their suppliers to significantly lower the costs of the products they purchase while also requiring them to take on work previously done by the customer without compensating them.
- Our higher education system has not evolved quickly enough in many cases to teach our emerging leaders what is known by successful human-centered practitioners.
- Talented young thought leaders in sustainability do not consider the impact they could have in manufacturing and instead set their sights on consulting businesses or government services. As a result, the industry primarily focuses on hiring from traditional employment pools.
- Deeply fractured local, regional, and national governments fail to provide necessary policy changes and support for responsible manufacturing programs.
- In cases where there is a recognition that things need to change, a lack of knowledge exists about moving toward a more desirable future state.

My nearly 30 years of manufacturing experience was that what had to get done each day was all-consuming. I went home each day, knowing that much work still needed to be done. I suspect that this is what most people in the industry also experience. So how can we break through the above issues that prevent other companies from becoming more sustainable?

WRITE A BOOK – BUILD A FRAMEWORK

After asking myself why more companies did not adopt sustainable manufacturing practices, I answered that maybe leaders needed to know how to move from the status quo to a more desirable future. So, I decided to write a book that weaves many insights from studying organizational excellence for over forty years and sustainability for the last fifteen years. My objective was to see commonalities among all business and manufacturing exemplars I admired and those I found unique. Similarly, I worked to assemble what I saw as the sequence of steps necessary to support owners and leaders of manufacturing plants to maximize their positive impact on their internal operations. Additionally, to positively impact their local community, region, and the world—my attempt to complete a BHAG, a Big Hairy Audacious Goal.

The intent of writing this book was to develop a framework encompassing what I see as the evolving elements of an exemplary manufacturing operation. There are many books on employee well-being, change management, coaching, leadership, management, manufacturing processes, organizational development, stakeholder theory, strategic management, sustainability, and so on. I saw a need for a book that laid out a framework that could shape the unique requirements for completing a significant manufacturing operation transformation for those in the early phases or those further down the path that could enhance the great work their organization was already doing. The book would not have all the answers but hopefully spark enthusiasm for the potential to create a better world through the power of business, particularly in the manufacturing industry.

Doing so has led to the development of a six-phase framework. The phases are:

The checklist format lays out the sequencing of the transformational work, where each phase builds upon the previous phase for this holistic framework for maximizing human welfare. For lean practitioners, they will see an ongoing pattern of the three stages of 1) evaluating the current state, 2) defining a desired future state, and 3) developing the plans to transition from the current state to the future state.

CLOSING COMMENTS

I hope you are intrigued about the potential of the manufacturing industry to make a transformational impact, not only for you as an individual but for your organization, your community, and the world. The question may be – How does one go from our status quo to becoming another manufacturing exemplar? The short answer is like eating a figurative elephant (the author does not condone the actual eating of elephants) – one bite at a time. However, a similar analogy is "the elephant in the room" how do I find the right figurative elephant to eat to meet my company's needs? Which bite should I take first, second, etc.? Why are we stuck on elephants? Please stop!!

I suggest that the answer is first to continue to read the balance of this book. Then, if the content inspires you, there is also the opportunity to take the available humanist manufacturing courses. Finally, if helpful, you can also work with me to help you find your path toward similar success to those profiled in this chapter. Each of the above exemplars defined a desired future state and worked the plans that evolved as they learned along the way. Their transformations have taken many years and are never-ending in all cases.

CHAPTER REFLECTION QUESTIONS

Did a particular industry exemplar interest you?

What about the exemplar's profile excited you?

What are you already doing, like the initiatives of the exemplars profiled in the chapter?

What could you adapt initially to improve your organization's environmental or social impact?

RECOMMENDED READING

Everybody Matters: The Extraordinary Power of Caring for People Like Family (2015) – Bob Chapman and Raj Sisodia – Portfolio / Penguin

Let My People Go Surfing: The Education of a Reluctant Businessman – Including 10 More Years of Business Unusual (2016) – Yvon Chouinard – Penguin Books

Mid-Course Correction Revisited: The Story and Legacy of a Radical Industrialist and His Quest for Authentic Change (2019) – Ray C. Anderson and John A. Lanier – Chelsea Green Publishing

Sustainability Leadership: A Swedish Approach to Transforming Your Company, Your Industry and the World (2020) – Henrik Henriksson and Elaine Weidman Grunewald – Palgrave Macmillan

PHASE 1

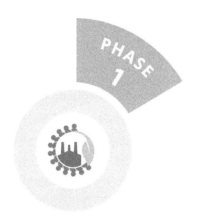

In this phase, we will begin Chapter 1 by reviewing definitions of humanism and humanistic principles. Next, we cover the ten humanist commitments that are the foundation of humanist manufacturing. Then, a humanist manufacturing vision statement and definition clarify how they apply within this framework.

CHAPTER 1
A HUMANIST PERSPECTIVE

"Our task must be to free ourselves by widening our circle of compassion to embrace all living creatures and the whole of nature and its beauty."

—ALBERT EINSTEIN

You might ask yourself why someone writes a book focusing on a human perspective. During my career, I learned the 5 Whys process. The process is to ask a question about why a problem exists. The answer may lead to another question. The pattern continues until an answer does not lead to another question. At that point, the root cause becomes apparent, a process that, on average, takes asking "why" five times. For me, the root cause behind the environmental and social harm done by manufacturing operations is a lack of proper leadership focus on the human aspect of all stakeholders impacted by their businesses.

I am a big fan of the CBS television series *Undercover Boss*.[1] High-level executives disguise themselves and take on various lower-level jobs to better understand what is happening within their businesses. The result is generally that the executives find out two things. The first is that things are not going well with revelations that corner office decisions lead to unintended consequences that negatively impact both the organization and the employees. The second is that many of their employees struggle at work and in their personal lives since they are financially unable to address the challenges they face due to earning less than a living wage. Unfortunately, we do not see how executive decisions impact their company's external stakeholders in the show.

Profit maximization has been a primary historical focus for business leaders, the objective being simply to maximize shareholder wealth with little to no other considerations. But in 1984, R. Edward Freeman, now of the University of Virginia Darden School of Business, wrote the book *Strategic Management: A Stakeholder Approach.*[2] He introduced the concept of "stakeholder theory, which emphasizes the interdependence of society and business and the need for organizations to create value for all who hold a stake in it — not just the shareholders."

A holistic stakeholder perspective is not only a shift from maximizing shareholder value to stakeholder focus but to maximizing stakeholder value. Stakeholder groups include, at a minimum, the customers, employees, government, lenders, local community, owners, society, and suppliers. Others can consist of a board of directors, competitors, distributors, media, Mother Nature, professional organizations, regulatory agencies, trade associations, unions, the world's ecological community, and certainly not to be forgotten, shareholders. As company owners or high-level executives, it is essential to understand the true impact of our business decisions on all stakeholders, human or otherwise.

Just as company executives in the *Undercover Boss* series experience first-hand what is happening, their new understanding should carry over to doing the same with all other stakeholders. Industry apparel manufacturers have historically only audited and monitored first-tier suppliers. Patagonia went deeper[3] and found in 2011 that there were multiple instances of worker exploitation, forced labor, and human trafficking at lower-level suppliers in their supply chain. As a founder and accredited member of the Fair Labor Association,[4] it was unacceptable. While embarrassing to this "well-heeled outdoor adventure brand," they responded by decreasing their number of first-tier suppliers, strengthening their social responsibility office, and contracting with Verité[5] to increase the number of audits at all levels of their supply chain. While one of many potential examples, upon discovering these deplorable human practices, Patagonia did not look the other way and instead chose to work to eliminate them.

Since humans have existed, so have philosophers who espouse society's need to integrate humanist principles. One could argue that not listening to these philosophers has seemingly led to some level of failure where global well-being suffers from environmental and social harm. Unfortunately, the business sector has caused some of the damage we see in the air, soil, and water pollution, climate change, global warming, income inequality, and wildlife destruction. The intent is not to pass judgment as these results were generally considered appropriate past practice. However, I believe that failing to take responsibility for our current practices and choosing not to improve upon them is no longer an acceptable option.

DEFINING HUMANISM AND HUMANIST PRINCIPLES

In this chapter, we will explore humanism and humanist principles. Humanism, which the American Humanist Association defines[6] as "A progressive philosophy of life that, without theism or other supernatural beliefs, affirms our ability and responsibility to lead ethical lives of personal fulfillment that aspire to the greater good." If you believe in theism or other supernatural beliefs like me, that part of the definition could be alarming. However, I am comfortable with the balance of the description that fits the intention of the humanist manufacturing framework. Generally, our manufacturing plants focus on achieving business objectives while complying with company values and beliefs and not whether or not our coworkers practice particular religious beliefs outside of work.

The author of the *Humanist Manifesto 2000: A Call for New Planetary Humanism*[7] states that "humanism is an ethical, scientific, and philosophical outlook that has changed the world." The Renaissance was the birth of humanism, leading to the beginnings of modern science developed at the beginning of the 17th century. The Enlightenment lasted between the 17th and 18th centuries and germinated social justice ideals as an ethical perspective based on universal human rights virtues, including freedom and happiness. There are seven universal commitments copied directly from the book:

1. *First, the underlying ethical principle of Planetary Humanism is the need to respect the dignity and worth of all persons in the world community.*
2. *Second, we ought to act to mitigate human suffering and increase the sum of human happiness.*
3. *Third, we should avoid an overemphasis on multicultural parochialism, which can be divisive and destructive.*
4. *Fourth, respect and concern for persons should apply to all human beings equally.*
5. *Fifth, these principles should apply to the world community of the present time, but also to the future.*
6. *Sixth, each generation has an obligation, as far as possible, to leave the planetary environment that it inherits a better place.*
7. *Seventh, we should take care to do nothing that would endanger the very survival of future generations.*

As fellow human beings, we are in a time of deep division that leads to an increasingly downward spiral of unhappiness. However, there is an opportunity to reverse the trend if we agree that these seven universal commitments are our collective responsibility and incorporate them into our actions. Whether or not we believe in the supernatural or theism, these seem to be commitments that make sense to incorporate into responsible business practices.

THE TEN HUMANIST COMMITMENTS

The humanist manufacturing framework integrates the *Ten Commitments of Living Humanist Values*[8] This content further resonated with me. A brief overview of the ten commitments is:

1. Altruism - I will help others in need without hoping for rewards.
Imagine the world if each person had a selfless concern for others while working to improve their well-being without expecting something in return. Instead, the welfare of others was a driving force to reinforce healthy connections to create better internal plant operations that supported thriving communities collectively and a better world.

2. Critical Thinking - I will practice good judgment by asking questions and thinking for myself.
There appears to be an increasing scarcity of critical thinking in the world. In addition, society faces a growing onslaught of information and misinformation. Therefore, a needed approach is to critically evaluate the available information, use reason to develop proper judgment, develop alternative solutions, and ultimately select the one that will most efficiently and effectively solve the issue.

3. Empathy - I will consider other people's thoughts, feelings, and experiences.
Individuals that are empathetic work at imagining what the other person is facing. In essence, stepping outside of ourselves and trying to experience their pain and suffering.

4. Environmentalism - I will take care of the Earth and the life on it.
The manufacturing industry can play a significant role in creating a healthier global environment. Companies can use *Cradle to Cradle*[9] designs to develop processes and products of significantly less or zero environmental harm. In addition, plant operations that desire to take their operations to the next level can adopt a regenerative production model and would benefit from reading the *Lessons for the Future: The Interface guide to changing the world.*[10]

5. Ethical Development - *I will always focus on becoming a better person.*
As children, we are introduced to cooperation, fairness, and sharing. As we mature, there is an opportunity to continue to evolve our ethical development. We can continually adapt and rebuild our moral frameworks as we constantly learn more about the world and our responsibility to develop into better human beings.

6. Global Awareness - *I will be a good neighbor to the people who share the Earth with me and help make the world a better place for everyone.*
As a child, I knew little beyond roughly a twenty-mile radius of the farm that was my home. However, I now know that forty percent of the world's population lives on $5.50 or less per day,[11] which requires us to develop better opportunities for our global citizens to experience healthy and dignified lives.

7. Humility - *I will be aware of my strengths and weaknesses and appreciate the strengths and weaknesses of others.*
The self-aware recognize their opportunity to contribute value to a work environment and where others bring different strengths to the group. Understanding that we are neither better nor worse than our coworkers allows the opportunity to express gratitude for the various roles that each member contributes to the organization.

8. Peace and Social Justice - *I will help people solve problems and handle disagreements in ways that are fair for everyone.*
To maintain a just work environment, we need to eradicate any level of injustice occurring to our internal and external stakeholders. We need to build a fair and equitable society for all individuals impacted by our business operations. The work needs to attain peace through effective and efficient conflict resolution, leading to restorative justice when harm occurs to individuals or groups.

9. Responsibility - I will be a good person—even when no one is looking—and own the consequences of my actions.
We must be willing to make the right choices regardless of the outcome and be ready to be accountable when we have made mistakes. While what others believe is right and wrong aligns with various codes of conduct, cultural values, expectations, and social mores, it is essential to clarify what is appropriate for the specific organization. Furthermore, creating an environment of caring and trust allows community members to come forward to work through issues that fall in the fuzzy area between clear right and wrong.

10. Service and Participation - I will help my community in ways that let me get to know the people I'm helping.
The approach to creating a better community should build on the previous nine commitments that add additional social awareness of the neighborhoods in which we operate. We can then use our unique capabilities to create thriving in the internal and external circles of company influence.

I know from experience that working for an employer that embraced only some of these commitments would have created a more favorable work experience for me. Furthermore, the manufacturing exemplars in the previous chapter appear to exhibit most of these humanist commitments. The planet we live on requires changes that will move us from a mindset of winners and losers. For example, the manufacturing industry faces significant challenges attracting and retaining employees. However, I believe an evolving humanist manufacturing framework can lead to better plant operations, thriving communities, and collectively a better world, making the industry more attractive to our younger generations.

Calls to inject humanism into business are not new, as found in the article *Business Does Not Need the Humanities — But Humans Do*.[12] Carvaka, Confucius, Gautama, and Socrates are just a few historical figures espousing humanism or humanistic thought. What is different at this point is that we live in increasingly challenging times rampant with opportunities to make a significant difference in improving the well-being of others.

Building on the theme of generating industry employment interest, younger generations want to be proud of their company and feel that their employer cares about them. They expect alignment with their values and the organization where they are employed. If not, they will soon begin looking for another opportunity to provide this for them. When employees feel valued, proud, and protected, their productivity and creativity soar – they rise above expectations and become engines of a company's innovation, growth, and profitability. In addition, the industry needs to attract and retain top talent in the manufacturing sector. Integrating humanist commitments into the leadership of factory operations can make that work meaningful and a career with enhanced purpose.

In her book, *Applied Humanism: How to Create More Effective and Ethical Businesses*,[13] Jennifer Hancock simplifies the definition as "A commitment that you make to yourself to be a good person." Hancock states that it is our choice to shift from the "false dichotomy" of the necessity of a heartless approach to business to avoid failure. My book will share many examples that support the reality that this past practice is untrue and without merit. She has four basic rules of humanist business management:

1. *Do no evil* – Global ethics studies have found that compassion is the top value for most people. Humanism bases decisions on compassion that acts as a moral compass where well-being as a primary metric should measure success, replacing the past priority of wealth. Most people are hard-wired to be compassionate. It is the basis of most religions and moral codes, allows people a common language to make ethical decisions, and makes us feel better.

2. *Reality matters* – Our brains have a natural resistance to fully determining reality. The brain allows us to make assumptions and generalize information. However, our

ability to use our sensory organs to analyze data properly has flaws. Our frame of reference and prior experiences inhibit our ability to perceive and interpret our reality accurately.

3. *Respect people* – Every human has the right to be treated with dignity and worth. A global population nearing eight billion comprises real individuals who deserve our compassion— switching from anger or hate for others to caring for all benefits those receiving a more dignified approach, leading to a happier world.

4. *It is your responsibility* – We must embrace responsibility as it is the key to attaining freedom. We have the choice of being "a victim of fate or the designer of our destiny." Success in life requires making good decisions. We cannot be happy if we make others miserable. Many of us desire a life of purpose. We can begin to live our lives intentionally by accepting our responsibility role. The outcome of effectively embracing responsibility is to live a stimulating life.

Her rules resonated with me as I unknowingly followed them in my leadership approach. The practices would also likely align with the manufacturing exemplars' work in leading their organizations to high levels of success. She writes that "adopting a humanist approach should help you think better, have better relationships, and feel more fulfilled" – seemingly something we should all at least be interested in exploring further, emphasizing the adoption of humanism in the manufacturing sector.

A HUMANIST MANUFACTURING APPROACH

Reflecting on all I have learned and experienced in my career and education, I imagined a vision for the manufacturing industry to invite those typically ignored as viable partners to engage as stakeholders. Building on Hancock's earlier humanism definition, we are making "A commitment to be a good manufacturing operation." Considering what that might mean led to the following vision statement:

The manufacturing industry allows each citizen of the world an oppor-tunity to meet their needs for just and healthy lives at a minimum, with a full opportunity to achieve their highest potential.

As the manufacturing industry faces many challenges, a revised way of managing plant operations will be required to draw our younger generations to this employment opportunity. As I worked on how to integrate humanist commitments into a manufacturing frame-work, I developed the following definition:

Humanist manufacturing focuses on the importance of integrated growth, moving toward self-actualization and transcendence for a production operation's internal and external stakeholders. The objec-tive is to establish an environment focused on strengths that promote upward spirals toward optimal individual and organizational perfor-mance. The work occurs in a positive whole system setting that compels the natural human tendency of innate good to motivate the organization's members to generate positive environmental and social impacts. Ultimately, it has the additional beneficial outcome of all stakeholders of its ecosystem doing well financially.

While a work in progress, it was a starting point to further improve the humanist manufacturing framework. Overall, this set of commit-ments resonated with me, and I believe it will resonate with others interested in developing manufacturing operations that positively impact their internal and external stakeholders.

CLOSING COMMENTS

We have reviewed several manufacturing operations leaders who have inspired me and many others to impact their stakeholders positively. We then looked at humanism from a general perspective: the teachings of ancient philosophers espousing society's need to integrate humanist principles. When we narrowed our focus to several approaches to adopting each of the ten humanist commitments into the humanist manufacturing framework, a thread emerged where it is apparent that each of the ten commitments is intertwined.

What excites me the most is that it would be difficult to argue that adopting these humanist commitments does not make sense for most manufacturing operations. A theme that recurred throughout the content is that effectively doing any of these commitments creates positive environmental and social impacts and, ultimately, a positive financial impact. Imagine how formidable an organization can become if it successfully adopts all ten humanist commitments. Using a humanist manufacturing lens, we will now move to actions that can improve the leaders of organizations and their management teams.

I am confident through my own experience, my academic research, and the success of many companies using elements of this approach that committing to the humanist commitment lens will:

- Attract and retain talented employees seeking jobs that allow them to reach their full potential while working for a company with similar values to their own.
- Engage and empower all stakeholders that see organizations' significant gains with a transformational vision.
- Delight customers who feel good about engaging with a humanist company while being cared for by highly engaged employees.
- Lead to efficient and effective operations as the workforce commits to achieving the compelling "why" for the company's existence.
- Increase profitability where doing the right thing to improve your company's environmental and social impacts will also enhance financial results.
- Expand the positive impact within the walls of your organization, the greater community, and collectively the world.

These outcomes will positively benefit all internal and external stakeholders of the organization. In addition, the coming chapters will deepen our understanding of applying these ten humanist commitments and how they will benefit a manufacturing operation that embeds them into their organization.

We will now transition to work through the Leadership Development phase in the upcoming chapters. Next, we will explore what is important to us as leaders using these humanist commitments to examine why they are in business and to define or further refine their company vision, mission, and values.

CHAPTER REFLECTION QUESTIONS

What was your initial reaction to the presentation of the humanist perspective?

Does the vision of Humanist Manufacturing resonate with you?

Which of the ten humanist commitments are already a part of your leadership style?

Which of them would you be interested in adopting?

Is the humanist perspective something about which you want to learn more?

RECOMMENDED READING

Applied Humanism: How to Create a More Effective and Ethical Business (2019) – Jennifer Hancock – Business Expert Press

Humanist Manifesto 2000: A Call to Action for a New Planetary Humanism (2000) – Paul Kurtz – Prometheus Books

PHASE 2

LEADERSHIP DEVELOPMENT

PHASE 2

2. Assessment, planning, and strengthening of the leadership group.

In this phase, the organization's owner(s) or primary leader works through an in-depth evaluation of their current capability to lead a transformative change initiative to become a humanist manufacturing operation. We are usually products of our education and experience. As a result, we are comfortable with our approach to business seen as successful by traditional measures. It is not until we experience a Ray Anderson "spear in the chest" epiphany or ask ourselves, "why can't work be fun" like Bob Chapman, that we see the need to reframe what we see as success for our manufacturing operations. As they say, "it begins at the top," so we begin with coaching for the owner or leader in Chapter 2.

Once an owner or leader has committed to integrating a human-centered approach throughout the organization, Chapter 3 guides the work to develop or enhance the company's "why," vision, mission, and values. Humanist commitments are the guideposts to building these vital elements of communicating the company's purpose to all internal and external stakeholders.

The in-depth leadership evaluation process begins again for the remaining executive team members in Chapter 3, first as individuals. Once this is complete, there should be an evaluation of team dynamics. The key is to plot the team's work styles and thinking preferences to understand the existing team's balance and address any misalignment with capabilities and the company strategy.

The work outlined in these three chapters places the leadership team in a position to successfully lead the organization to higher levels of positive stakeholder impact.

CHAPTER 2
KNOWING THYSELF

"You might have much of the world's riches, and you might hold a portion of authority, but if you have no Ubuntu, you do not amount to much."

—Archbishop Desmond Tutu

My wife introduced me to the Ubuntu[1] philosophy about 18 months before I began developing the initial humanist manufacturing framework. The philosophy is an African belief that " we owe our selfhood to others, that, if you will, no man/woman is an island." William E. Flippin Jr., an advocate for justice, ecumenist, and grassroots organizer, further shares that Ubuntu is "a deeply personal philosophy that calls on us to mirror our humanity for each other." For Africans living in Ubuntu, this means treating others with openness, personal dignity, unquestioning cooperation, warmth, and willing participation - a leadership style aligning well with our humanist commitments.

While all ten humanist commitments from the previous chapter are not implicit, it is not a reach to believe these are integral to this philosophy. Similarly, a person does not need to score a hypothetical 10 of ten points for each commitment for a perfect score of 100 to be a humanist manufacturing leader. Instead, what is important is to assess our current capability and how to further improve ourselves as leaders capable of guiding an organization to becoming a humanist manufacturing operation.

Much like a building cannot be built on an unstable foundation, the work to become a more humanist manufacturing operation should begin with an overall leader assessment. Whether new to the job or seasoned leaders, we can benefit from taking an inventory of our current approach to leading an organization and determining a personal growth plan. Therefore, instead of beginning at the organization's top, we will flip this perspective to one where it starts at the bottom.

The organization leader should complete a comprehensive personal assessment using the foundation analogy. Leaders who truly understand the individual attributes they bring to their work can more efficiently and effectively build the base to facilitate transformative success for their organizations. The perspective needed to maximize this leadership assessment work will be to focus on the positive, be truly honest with ourselves, be willing to accept feedback from others and be interested in adopting or more fully integrating the humanist commitments. Leaders willing to do so have a more significant opportunity to create a work environment where each stakeholder can maximize their potential for the collective betterment of all. An employee-centric environment stimulates creativity and innovation, allowing ideas to blossom into reality through free-flowing communication.

SHIFTING FROM THE NEGATIVE TO THE POSITIVE

I began my career in machine repair and rebuilding in the manufacturing industry. My employer was a company that bought and sold new and used machinery and did repair and overhaul work of manufacturing equipment for customers. As you can imagine, my job was often to find out what was wrong with a down machine or line and get it back into production as quickly as possible.

Over the years, I transitioned into engineering and plant management roles, initially continuing the trend to focus on what was wrong.

It might be solving a quality concern, finding a replacement for an absent employee, or expediting a late shipment to a customer. In most cases, it was an all-hands on deck to resolve whatever negative issue we were facing, often at other projects' expense. But unfortunately, it seemed to perpetuate a downward negative spiral of one crisis after another.

I adopted the positive lens approach during my last plant manager assignment. Unfortunately, when I arrived, the plant was experiencing significant downtime and quality problems, and most production lines failed to make their daily production rate. Applying a positive perspective, I would go to the whiteboards at the end of each line, where the line leader posted the various production results for each shift. I would look for favorable results and write comments about them. It was difficult to do early on, but there was increasingly good news as the weeks and months passed.

I began to routinely have line leaders come to me smiling from ear to ear to share they "made rate" during that shift. Our quality defects went down, productivity increased, and machine uptime improved. If I was away or returned to the plant late and went home without writing these notes, they would ask me why none were left the previous day when I returned. It was not the only change we made, but I know that focusing on what the hourly workforce was doing right was a key driver in our success. Think about your own experiences – did you achieve the most in a positive or negative environment?

One might think that there is no need to shift from determining what is wrong but instead focusing on what is right with our organizations. However, my experience has found this a primary key to maximizing organization potential in multiple environments where I have engaged as a manager and consultant. Thus, I encourage leaders looking for extraordinary performance from their company to approach the work by leading positively. Cameron and Wooten[2] of the Center for Positive Organizations in the University of Michigan Ross School of Business developed four positive leadership strategies to include:

1. *Enabling positive relationships* – Leaders benefit from creating positive energy through facilitation and modeling positivity. The work includes diagnosing and building energy networks by identifying positive energizers. Then, they are supported and rewarded for tasks or filling roles for interaction, coaching, and mentoring others to expand the desired energy networks. The result is stronger interpersonal relationships that lead to deeper coordination and cooperation through efficient relationships that result in higher individual and organizational performance.

2. *Enabling a best-self feedback process* – Positive reinforcement will see heightened relationships with higher cohesion and mutual support. Again, results should focus on the highest talents and capabilities of the employees in their areas of responsibility.

3. *Enabling positive communication* – Affirmative and supportive language becomes the norm to replace a negative and critical focus as the single key factor for achieving tremendous organizational success. A study of top management teams discovered that they engaged in a 5.6 to 1 ratio of favorable to unfavorable statements. Those with average performance had a ratio of 1.85 to 1, and poor-performing teams came in at a .36 to 1 ratio – a culture of negativity that yielded negative results

4. *Enabling positive meaning* – Establishing a culture where people feel a profound purpose positively impacts employees by reducing absenteeism, depression, dissatisfaction, and turnover. Focusing on the positive further increases commitment, effort, empowerment, engagement, fulfillment, happiness, and satisfaction. Those seeking employment with a purpose are looking for a calling to do a greater good.

The power of positivity is real. The evidence is apparent in the scientific studies and an experience I have seen first-hand as a plant manager. When paired with emotional intelligence, working to increase our positive perspective has more impact.

THE BENEFITS OF EMOTIONAL INTELLIGENCE

Our ability to understand the human brain continues to evolve as further research and technological capabilities allow additional insight into this complex organ. For example, we have recently begun to understand the role of mirror neurons, which fire both when we act and when we see it performed in others, thus enabling higher concepts like connection and compassion that employees can learn through mimicry.[3] Therefore, leaders must understand how to recognize, understand, and manage our feelings to effectively and efficiently identify, understand, and influence the emotions of those in our care responsibly.

The leadership of an organization can create a more engaged workforce by strengthening overall emotional intelligence (EI). Maximizing our EI capability as leaders leads to a strategic advantage of increasing job satisfaction, resulting in higher individual and team performance. These benefits[4] are an outcome of:

1. Being more empathetic during difficult conversations.
2. Managing our emotions and those of our coworkers during stressful or overwhelming situations.
3. Enhancing conflict resolution.
4. Strengthening our ability to motivate and coach the workforce.
5. Increasing employee collaboration potential.
6. Building an environment of psychological safety.

Understanding that emotions precede thought is key to improving the potential for ourselves and others to achieve greater levels of success in our personal and professional lives. If these benefits are desirable, we should look at an overview of EI.

THE ELEMENTS OF EI

Daniel Goleman and Richard Boyatzis share that EI comprises[5] four domains and twelve elements:

1. Self-awareness – The ability to recognize emotions and how they shape our response to what is occurring in our environment.
  1) Emotional self-awareness

2. Self-management – The ability to manage emotions healthily, adapt to changing circumstances, control impulsive thoughts, and complete commitments.
  2) Emotional self-control
  3) Adaptability
  4) Achievement orientation
  5) Positive outlook

3. Social awareness – The ability to empathetically interact with others by recognizing environmental cues and power dynamics when working to establish group comfort.
  6) Empathy
  7) Organizational awareness

4. Relationship management – The establishment of stronger bonds in our interactions by inspiring and influencing the workforce through clear communication leading to high-performance teams void of conflict.
  8) Influence
  9) Coach and mentor
  10) Conflict management
  11) Teamwork
  12) inspirational leadership

. . .

These leading EI practitioners recommend assessment tools to include the 360-degree assessment that will help gauge one's current capability in this crucial leadership area. They further suggest working with an expert who can improve areas that need strengthening.

AN EI CASE STUDY

A three-year study[6] of Amadori, a European food manufacturing supplier to McDonald's, asked three questions:

1. *Does emotional intelligence affect individual performance?*
2. *Does emotional intelligence affect organization engagement?*
3. *Does organizational engagement impact organizational performance?*

The results found that EI predicted:

1. Forty-seven percent of the variation in the performance scores of managers.
2. A strong correlation between increased organizational engagement and EI explains 76% of the variation by a manager.
3. Improvement of the bottom line through higher organizational engagement.

An additional benefit was a 63% reduction in employee turnover of the sales force during the study period attributed to the emphasis on enhancing EI skills. Enhancing managerial EI competencies through personal development led to a corporate culture better capable of dealing with change and complexity.

The emergence of a different understanding of the human brain allows us to implement further improvement plans to develop our EI skills. Savvy leaders will embrace emotional intelligence to reframe their ability to positively impact employee job satisfaction and performance. With proper help, we can improve these essential capabilities necessary to lead effectively with empathy and compassion. The potential for increasing individual performance that enhances organizational engagement with a resulting better bottom line should entice us to embrace EI fully.

KNOWING OUR PERSONALITY TYPE

Another way to better know ourselves is the use of personality-type instruments. Over the years, I have done the Meyers-Briggs type indicator, the CliftonStrengths assessment, the DISC assessment, and the Herrmann Brain Dominance Instrument (HBDI)® psychometric assessment. Another with a high recommendation from a friend is The Predictive Index. Each tool has a scientific basis and a long track record of success in helping individuals learn to understand themselves better.

I have often wondered why others did not see what seemed evident to me during my career. I was further confused about why it was not well received when sharing this insight with my various bosses. The answer to this bewilderment came from a recent Clifton-Strengths assessment. My top strength was analytical, which was not a surprise. The value came in the follow-up report feedback on blind spots.

Individuals with analytical insight can uncover the essential facts necessary to realize excellence. The mindset is not a plan but to search for patterns and connections. They bring a logical and objective approach to finding simplicity in complexity. Analysts use systematic reasoning to develop more innovative concepts than the other team members. The analyst wants to see data as value-free and aligning with their objective and dispassionate approach to finding the most significant outcome.

Those with an analytical approach begin a questioning process to determine if a proposed theory is sound. Analysts have a refining mind that will continue to ask questions until the theory either withers and dies or is a logical path to achieve the desired result. They want to expose "wishful or clumsy thinking." Their objective is to absorb and analyze information to help the team make better decisions.

Again, the feedback that "analytical" was my top strength was not a revelation to me as it aligns with my approach to work. The report's value was that I must understand that other team members will have a personal, subjective, and emotional attachment to their proposed theories. Instead of delivering what I perceive as objective and dispassionate advice, it comes across as critical and skeptical.

It would have been good to have known forty years ago that I appear to doubt the validity of the ideas of others. I presented as lacking trust in them and being a difficult coworker. While I thought I was trying to stretch our thinking, it was a problem for my colleagues. As leaders, we must know what we currently do not know about ourselves. Adding a personality assessment or two can provide additional insight into what we learn through the 360-degree evaluation. A willingness to be open and accepting of the results is vital in our understanding of who we are and how to improve our ability to lead others.

Most jobs these days require a great deal of time and energy. Gone are the days of a traditional eight-hour workday where part of it was occupied with rounds of golf with a customer, followed by long martini lunches. Add in that technology has us accessible to the company 24/7/365, and there is little time left for many to spend time with their family, exercise, and pursue hobbies. The result is that there is little opportunity to expand one's knowledge base beyond what crosses the desk in our fast-based world.

EXPANDING OUR KNOWLEDGE BASE

Leaders of an organization should assess their understanding of the current and future state of leading-edge business practices in their field. The "Knowledge Half-Life"[7] was introduced fifty years ago by Fritz Machlup. The concept was the amount of time that half of the existing knowledge becomes obsolete or superseded. Buckminster Fuller had a similar idea of the amount of time it takes for knowledge to double. The estimate was that this happened every 12-13 months in

1982. Recent estimates are that knowledge is doubling every 12 hours. Therefore, influential leaders must develop ways to monitor and adopt relevant business knowledge to keep pace with this rapid growth.

Generally, the more we learn, the more we understand how little we know about any topic. Given the rapid growth of knowledge, we need to continue to develop our expertise in our chosen field. A list of recommendations[8] for expanding our expertise includes:

1. *Listen like a beginner* – Leaders increase their effectiveness when they listen to the needs of their communities. Then they can better understand their current knowledge and what else needs to be known to help address these concerns.
2. *Simplify complex issues* – Distill knowledge sharing in a manner that is easy to grasp by the intended audience using efficient and effective communication.
3. *Keep learning* – Learning is a lifetime commitment, given the rapid knowledge growth rate.
4. *Check your ego* – View knowledge sharing as an opportunity to contribute to the goal. We should work to avoid overconfidence and keep self-importance in check.
5. *Cultivate communication skills* – Continue to evolve the ability to share your knowledge with the organization.

Doing these in an empathetic manner allows leaders to share knowledge beneficially with others. Like anything worthwhile, adopting these recommendations will take time and effort further to integrate them into the work of a leader.

An example of someone using the empathetic expert approach is Ray Anderson. An Interface sales representative was asked by a customer what they were doing for the environment. His initial thought was that his company was complying with all regulations, so there was no need to change their manufacturing approach. Using his current knowledge base, that was a reasonable assessment. However, instead of standing pat, he gained additional insight to transform Interface into an industry leader in sustainable manufacturing. Knowing he needed to learn more led to developing an Eco Dream

Team.[9] The group included authors, activists, entrepreneurs, and scientists. They defined the vision of the "Seven Fronts" of Mount Sustainability by working together. The framework included zero waste to landfills, zero fossil fuel energy use, zero process water use, and zero greenhouse gas emissions. The tracking mechanism of EcoMetrics measured the energy and materials flow in and out of the company.

The story of Ray Anderson, a then 60-year-old man, completely embracing the need to go from "complying with the law" to a leader in sustainability needed telling. From his first speech to a staff task force at his organization to later doing 100[10] speeches a year, he began a ministry of the value of adopting a zero-impact business model. The financial results were equally impressive. Their stock price went from $2 per share in 2000 to $18 in 2007, with sales exceeding $1 billion annually – a beautiful result. Doing the right thing has also driven long-term financial success that continues as an ongoing manufacturing exemplar. Anderson is one example of many leaders who have allowed themselves to continue to grow their knowledge base and deepen it for the benefit of their organization. As a result, opportunities abound with ongoing advances in employee well-being, materials, processes, products, technology, and sustainability that we will explore in subsequent chapters.

KEY SUPPORT

A leader can benefit from working with an executive coach. The work to significantly transform an organization begins with changing ourselves as leaders. Working with a coach can help to keep a proper focus on further developing critical skills for leadership that include:

- Ability to gain additional perspective from an outsider.
- Better listening skills.
- Confidence from support in the refinement of organizational plans before launch.
- Creation of an optimal work culture.
- Deeper self-awareness.
- Development of clear and effective communication.

- Enhanced job and life satisfaction.
- Guidance in goal setting and personal development.
- Improvement of speaking and presentation skills.
- Increased effectiveness through more robust time management.
- More strategic risk-taking.
- Support in developing personal empowerment.
- Teaching and mentoring.
- Team building and talent management.

The work to enhance leadership performance can be accelerated when a leader engages with a well-matched coach. Developing a growth mindset allows leaders to see obstacles that may currently prevent personal improvement. Empathy for the challenges others face in their development can emerge. The leader can better leverage individual strengths. Ultimately, the expectation of self-improvement becomes the norm for the balance of the organization's members.

A global study[11] by the Institute of Executive Coaching and Leadership (IECL) found five well-being benefits for individuals receiving coaching:

- A 9.5% increase in optimism about the future.
- Improvement of 18.5% in the ability to relax.
- A 12.7% increase in better problem resolution.
- The power of 10.9% more in clearer thinking.
- A 16.7% improvement in healthier and stronger relationships.

An example of success by IECL is their work with GlaxoSmithKline: over five years was a 2,900% increase in coaching with the organization with a return on investment of $66 million (US dollars).

CLOSING COMMENTS

We need to know ourselves better to lead companies that are the employer of choice. But unfortunately, as I travel around and visit various plant operations, it appears that too many leaders are suffering from the tale of the boiling frog. Leaders once in cold water have had the heat increase gradually over time, whereas now they are at a point where the water is near a temperature that will lead to negative consequences. I encourage those in the near-boiling pot of water to step out and view their circumstances from an outsider's perspective. We should question everything that is status quo to appropriately gauge what needs to change to be a relevant champion of humanist manufacturing.

CHAPTER REFLECTION QUESTIONS

Is your leadership perspective positive, negative, or somewhere in between?

What is your current leadership style?

What strengths do you bring to your role as the organization's leader?

Are you creating a culture of legal and ethical behavior? Do your actions demonstrate this commitment?

Are you willing to incorporate societal well-being and benefit into your work?

Is there interest in actively supporting and strengthening your local community?

Is becoming a sustainable or regenerative manufacturing operation based on humanist commitments vital to you?

What is your current approach to personal development? Should it be enhanced?

Before you are ready to lead your company through transformative change, is there personal growth you need to embrace?

How does the adoption of humanist commitments shift your thoughts on the content of this chapter?

RECOMMENDED READING

Emotional Intelligence: 25th Anniversary Edition (2020) – Daniel Goleman – Bloomsbury Publishing

Now, Discover Your Strengths: The Revolutionary Gallup Program that Shows You How to Develop Your Unique Talents and Strengths 20th Anniversary Edition (2020) – Marcus Buckingham and Donald O. Clifton – The Free Press

The Happiness Advantage: The Seven Principles That Fuel Success and Performance at Work (2010) - Shawn Achor – Crown Business

The Whole Brain Business Book, Second Edition: Unlocking the Power of Whole Brain Thinking in Organizations, Teams, and Individuals, 2nd Edition (2015) – Ned Herrmann and Ann Herrmann-Nehdi – McGraw-Hill Education

CHAPTER 3
WHY, VISION, MISSION, AND VALUES

"Your purpose in life is to find your purpose and give your whole heart and soul to it."

—GAUTAMA BUDDHA

Revisiting the introduction to the book in Chapter 1, we will explore the importance of a well-defined "why" in creating excitement to get out of bed each morning and go to work. Whether a new startup or a long-running firm, the owner or leader should define the "why" for being in business. If the goal is to make money for your gain, that will not be compelling to the organization's stakeholders.

GETTING TO OUR "WHY"

In his book *Start with Why: How Great Leaders Inspire Everyone to Take Action*[1] and TED Talk[2] *How leaders inspire action*, Simon Sinek's focus on "why" businesses exist has been viewed more than 59 million times. His Golden Circle has an outer ring where he posits that organizations know "What" products and services they provide to customers. The middle ring is the "How" they produce them. The difference he found is that most influential leaders inspired people by reaching an inner circle of effectively communicating "Why" they did the work they had chosen to accomplish.

Reflecting on my career, I realized I had not worked for companies with a clearly defined "Why." The owners would have quickly answered the "What" and "How" aspects of the business. However, they likely were never encouraged to take things to a more profound "why" level. Sinek found that successful companies who understand their "why" did not learn it as a part of their business student curriculums.

A personal example of someone knowing "why" he stated a business is my friend Michael Pirron. He had a career in consulting, where he was well compensated, but the work left him feeling unfulfilled. During his MBA work in the Kellogg School of Management at Northwestern University, he developed his idea of a social enterprise built on Newman's Own model of "all profits to charity." In 2006, with $50 and a laptop, he founded Impact Makers as a for-profit IT and management consulting firm. It was and continues to be a hybrid of the best of the for-profit and nonprofit business models where he chose to give away 100% of profits. In 2015, they took things to another level by donating 100% of company equity to The Community Foundation and Virginia Community Capital.

Pirron wanted to develop a company to resolve two fundamental issues — the lack of time most professionals had to make a substantial difference in their community and nonprofits' need to fundraise." The result was a social venture that:

- Provides professional consulting services at market prices.
- Competes to win business.
- Pays employee's market rates.
- Maximizes profits.
- Retains a volunteer board of directors.
- Is transparent with all stakeholders and shares financials publicly.

- Contributes pro bono consulting and gives all profits to charitable community organizations over the company's lifetime.
- Provides a minimum pledge to a nonprofit partner — even when not profitable.

While the company continues to evolve the business model, it primarily exists as what he saw as his original "why." During the research I conducted at his company, a recurring theme during interviews of their various stakeholders was that this was why they were attracted to the company. There was a strong sense of pride when sharing the importance of working for a company with a well-defined "why." I witnessed first-hand the impact of having this defined clearly for an organization.

What I experienced at Impacts Makers and the stories of the manufacturing exemplars shared in Chapter 1 and others I have read about helped me define my "why." First, I see it as using the work experience and knowledge gained in manufacturing and academia to better understand past environmental and social damage. Then, build on this work to create and help apply humanist manufacturing commitments to better the lives of some of the world's stakeholders.

CLEARLY SEEING THE FUTURE

Once the "why" is defined, an important next step is to develop a vision for the organization. The owner or leader should create a succinct verbal description of what the company would look like upon achieving the vision. A well-developed vision inspires the organization's stakeholders and becomes the North Star to guide everyone on an intentional course toward the desired destination. The journey does not end as the needs of our stakeholders evolve, but a well-crafted vision can be timeless.

In his book *Leading Change*,[3] John Kotter defines vision as: "a picture of the future that implies or comments on why people should work to create this future." He describes three purposes the vision serves:

1. The direction of change clarifies hundreds or thousands of decisions.
2. The organization's stakeholders are motivated to engage in actions, including some that may be painful, to work strategically to achieve the vision.
3. The collective actions are aligned to efficiently and effectively reach the vision.

The organizations I studied that I would define as successful companies develop strategic initiatives as coordinated and targeted activities executed with legitimate urgency to make vision achievement possible. A vision that presents a desirable and straightforward verbal picture communicates it so that employees can imagine it as feasible with a timelessness that allows the flexibility the organization will need to achieve tremendous success.

The ultimate result is for organizations to develop transformational visions, defined as a complete and positive change that provides a bright future state for all stakeholders. However, if we do not want to "aim too low and reach it," let us explore how to aim higher – beyond traditional visions of success to thriving for all stakeholders impacted by manufacturing operations.

Imagine the impact the manufacturing sector could make if we developed work environments that maximize the potential of all stakeholders. What seems unlikely is possible per the results that industry exemplars are achieving with guidance from their visions:

- Berry-Wehmiller - "We measure success by the way we touch the lives of people."
- General Motors - "To create a future of zero crashes, zero emissions, and zero congestion, and we have committed ourselves to lead the way toward this future."
- H2 Green Steel – "To undertake the global steel industry's greatest ever technological shift. We are committed to accelerating change by eliminating almost all CO_2 emissions from the steel production process. We are starting from

scratch, building a large-scale, hydrogen-based, and digital native company."

Each example provides their organizations a North Star to guide the thousands of decisions, motivate their workforces to engage in their visions, and align their actions efficiently and effectively to achieve the desired goal.

HOW THE WORK IS DONE

The mission is the ongoing work that should help the organization realize the defined transformational vision. Research[4] by Gallup found that only one-third of US workers strongly agree that their organization's mission is essential to them. The manufacturing sector was ten percentage points lower in the "strongly agree" category. Gallup states that manufacturing executives recognize the potential to improve operations by enhancing employee mission engagement. While they know this has potential, they are seemingly unsuccessful at achieving the desired improvement given the previously shared results, leading them to believe that their employees do not care. Cheesy posters and taglines urging employees with "**T**ogether **E**veryone **A**chieve **M**ore" are failing.

The Gallup author has found that workers respond to initiatives favorable to their communities. Her nearly ten years of consulting in plants have led to a common theme: workers connect to missions that help their neighborhoods. In addition, they want good-paying jobs that allow them to do great things for their community. When corporate mission can align with local communities, the employees become more motivated to engage in their success. In other words, a poster telling employees that they're "doing great things" is not nearly as meaningful as one that tells them they're "doing great things for [the town in which the plant is located]."

What I see as an inspirational mission is the following:

- Interface – "An abiding commitment to show that sustainability is better for business. We believe that change starts with us and is transforming Interface from a plunderer of the earth to an agent of its restoration. Through this process of redesigning ourselves, we hope to be a catalyst for the redesign of global industry."

While Interface does not address the neighborhood aspect in the preceding paragraphs, I know enough about the organization that they have a history of high-level engagement success as a desirable member of their communities. Therefore, we will further explore how manufacturing plants can integrate the betterment of their neighborhoods into their missions to create value for all of their stakeholders.

KNOWING WHAT WE VALUE MOST

If you have worked through a values ranking exercise, you soon learn how difficult it can be to narrow the list to four to five, of which there is no compromise. In a Harvard Business Review article,[5] Lencioni shares a list of values: Communication, Respect, Integrity, and Excellence, values most of us would agree are essential for a company to uphold. Our top company values might differ, but these would be considered. Unfortunately, Enron – an American energy company found guilty of accounting and corporate fraud – espoused these values without upholding them.[6] The result was one of the most significant bankruptcy filings in the history of the United States of a company holding more the $60 billion in assets. Enron proves Lencioni's point: an extreme example of how hollow values are meaningless.

Lencioni instead recommends that organizations organize values into four categories of values:

1. *Core values* – Deeply ingrained values that are never compromised, even at the cost of short-term gain. The cultural cornerstones are inherent and inalienable in guiding company actions. A classic case is the 1982 Tylenol crisis faced by Johnson & Johnson, now a model for effective corporate crisis management.[7]

2. *Aspirational values* – One or more currently missing values that will support the transformational vision. These should be limited so that they do not dilute the core values. For example, Ray Anderson of Interface had his "spear in the chest" epiphany moment. He adopted the purpose of making his company a sustainability leader,[8] becoming a firmly entrenched aspirational value.

3. *Permission-to-play values* – Setting the minimum social standards that the organization requires. A key opportunity to ensure organizations hire and retain engaged employees is to share upfront what the company will expect. My experience is that this seldom occurs. I know that I did not ask my potential employers what their minimum expectations would be of me. Instead, we must provide a guiding set of expectations around things like job flexibility, expectations of working overtime, and how we expect coworkers to treat one another.

4. *Accidental values* – The common interests and personalities of the employees have the potential to become unintended values without proper leadership focus. For example, the ownership or executive team may expect the organization members to treat internal and external stakeholders with integrity. However, if they emphasize profitability, the managers may begin to cut corners and act dishonestly to meet the profit margin expectations.

Johnson & Johnson's (J&J) response to the Tylenol Killer[9] crisis in 1982 was an example of sticking to its core values. An unknown individual injected cyanide into Extra-Strength Tylenol capsules, which resulted in seven deaths. The J&J chairman, James Burke, recalled 31 million bottles of Tylenol capsules from store shelve during this timeframe. He replaced them with safer Tylenol tablets, the first of many actions that cost more than $100 million. In addition, the company held to the credo of its "moral responsibility to society beyond sales and profit." Burke did not waver from the long-held J&J values as they developed the overall response to the crisis. Ultimately, J&J doing the right things in a time of difficulty led the company on a path to becoming a pharmaceutical powerhouse.

While the J&J and Enron examples are the extremes, they represent the importance of living by the defined values of an organization. For the values to make an impact, they must become integrated into the day-to-day activities of an organization's employees. The owner or leader of the company must monitor company activities to see that all decisions, from small to large, align with its stated values. The workforce also needs to see ongoing evidence of this same approach routinely taken by the leadership group. Then, when a crisis arises, the immediate response should align with the company's strong values.

Cascade Engineering embraces the following values:[10]

- *Triple bottom line* – They have developed a culture focusing on People, Planet, and Profit. They work with stakeholders to achieve operational success using a business model where all thrive.
- *Empowered people* – Treat employees with dignity and respect regardless of racial, cultural, or individual differences in an inclusive work environment using courage and consideration.
- *Trust* – Building an entrepreneurial mindset that is transparent and honest in interactions with all stakeholders. A strong culture that believes in the good of people with a requirement of conducting all interactions at the highest level of legal, ethical, and moral integrity.
- *Innovation* – A willingness to experiment in an environment devoid of fear that embraces innovation as vital to long-term growth driven by a passion for creating unique and sustainable processes, programs, products, and services.
- *Excellence* – Through the Cascade Enterprise System, the organization utilizes world-class talent to foster a culture that strives for impeccability in talent, skills, and equipment.

Their company strives to create an inclusive work environment where all stakeholders have the opportunity to achieve mutual success.

The values of Cascade Engineering benefit the communities where they work and live. The resultant culture attracts high-caliber new employees and helps retain those who see the organization's values in action each day.

CLOSING COMMENTS

Whether a startup or a long-term operation, I agree with Simon Sinek about the importance of developing our "why." An organization with an inspirational "why" will attract talented people. A well-developed and articulated transformational vision is key to the success of a leadership team getting all stakeholders engaged in creating the desired future state of the business. Understanding the mission guides the organization's members as they work daily to realize the vision. The values define the expectations of appropriate actions in carrying out the mission.

You know that you are successful when it envelopes all of the senses and permeates all interactions of those involved with the organization. The potential for ultimate success is maintaining no dissent or doubt as employees work together to achieve the desired result. The successful leader will understand that this requires a reciprocal relationship where all parties give and receive a genuine and authentic commitment to one another.

CHAPTER REFLECTION QUESTIONS

Can you concisely share your "why" compellingly with your internal and external stakeholders?

Are you meeting the expectations of your employees?

Does the current vision inspire key stakeholders to achieve transformational change?

Does the vision include an all-stakeholder perspective?

Is the company mission clearly defined?

Are the values defined, and is there evidence of full integration into the culture?

Are all of these in alignment with legal and ethical behavior?

Have the humanist commitments been integrated into your thinking about developing "why," vision, mission, and values?

RECOMMENDED READING

Start with Why: How Great Leaders Inspire Everyone to Take Action (2011) – Simon Sinek – Portfolio / Penguin

The Business Romantic: Give Everything, Quantify Nothing, and Create Something Greater Than Yourself (2015) – Tim Leberecht – Harper Business

CHAPTER 4

KNOWING THY EXECUTIVE TEAM

"It doesn't make sense to hire smart people and tell them what to do:
we hire smart people so they can tell us what to do."

—STEVE JOBS

A leader is only as good as the people surrounding them. My experience aligns with the research that leaders must fill an essential role in creating efficient and effective manufacturing operations. The leader must set the initial direction and then inspire and champion the executive team members with the proper responsibility and authority to do the work well.

Successful leaders shift from thinking that no one else can do the work and instead begin to develop the employees in their care to improve continually. A common theme for organizations that struggle is the burden of micro-managers. As a result, the company slowly erodes to lower performance levels as people wait for direction. The issue results in further negative consequences when it becomes better for employees to avoid decisions than to make a wrong one occasionally. As things bog down, the leader intensifies their micro-management, leading to an increasingly negative downward spiral.

The hope is that the current or future leader that has made it to this point in the book will agree with the value of self-assessment. Furthermore, the individual will have a sense of a leadership approach that will bring out the best in the organization, creating a work environment of inspired employees focused on delighting customers. At a minimum, the leader would work with the leadership team members through the same "Knowing Thyself" process in Chapter 3 as individuals. Even more significant potential exists when the executive management team works through the process collectively. I see this as essential to develop themselves into a cohesive unit before moving to the next phase of a company transformation. The value in doing so emerges in the balance of this chapter.

UNDERSTANDING TEAM DYNAMICS

Several options exist for personality-type instruments that can also be useful in better understanding and leveraging team dynamics. Taking this work to the team level is a holistic approach that leads to better outcomes as the organization works to transform its operation. Understanding one another better, leveraging existing strengths, adding additional talent to fill in gaps, and committing to the direction of the owner or leader allows the potential of a high-performing team to achieve more significant accomplishments. We will review three personality types that include a team focus: CliftonStrengths, Herrmann Brain Dominance Instrument, and the Predictive Index.

A review of the CliftonStrengths for the team is one opportunity to increase the impact of the leadership team.[1] Key benefits include increased productivity and sales, higher engagement, and lower attrition. When team members have reviewed their CliftonStrengths 34[2] report, everyone understands what they do best as individuals and how it fits the other leadership team members. The members can further know the blind spots of themselves and their peers to improve team interactions. A proper environment will allow them to lift one another to a higher level of individual and collective performance.

For this work to have the most significant impact, it must use positive psychology principles. Meaningful conversations to better understand one another as team members require us to understand the strengths we bring to the team. When everyone views the group through this lens, there is a more potent opportunity for tremendous success. From this perspective, the group can ask what can improve teamwork, team dynamics, and team collaboration. The beneficial results range from 7%-23% higher employee engagement, 8%- 18% increased performance, and 20%-73% lower attrition—a double win of greater workplace satisfaction and a better bottom line.

A strengths-based team approach supported by the Clifton-Strengths assessment results allows for a decisive shift in the collective mindset. More excellent performance is possible when team members work together. We can optimize collaboration and team dynamics. The results further provide a common language and vocabulary that allows team members to understand one another better. The potential synergy increases for the team as members follow their passions, which leads to increased energy and more outstanding performance. A workplace culture emerges that attracts and retains high-caliber talent. While the bottom line is potentially enhanced, the overall quality of life vastly improves.

The assessment results also provide evidence of each team member's strengths in an objective form. Employee development has more significant potential using the provided information to improve employee engagement and development. Shifting from what is wrong with an employee to one based on strengths can result in a positive coaching experience. As we lift each team member's strengths, the overall dynamic is a more engaged team using a strengths-based approach to implement the action steps necessary to realize the transformational vision.

The next personality type of interest is the Herrmann Brain Dominance Instrument. The value of understanding our (HBDI)® assessment results is to understand ourselves as individuals better and benefit from knowing the mental preferences of our team members. Their leadership playbook[3] lists reasons we should value diversity of thought from the four quadrants, including:

- Guard against expert confidence and groupthink.

- Scale new insights to higher levels.
- Assign the best employee to the most pressing problems
  faced by the organization.

Each leadership team member brings different mental processes regarding how they prefer to think, attack initiatives, cooperate, and their perspective on new opportunities. Since our preferences also guide how we view others, it is easy to overlook and understand the value of other perspectives if they are considered radical to our own. As leaders, we must recognize our blind spots and embrace the concept that a wide range of thinking preferences applied adequately to the various tasks to run the organization is an optimal business practice.

The HBDI Whole Brain® Model includes four types of thinking preferences that organize how the brain functions:

- A Quadrant – Analytical and logical.
- B Quadrant – Detailed and structured.
- C Quadrant – Participatory and people-oriented.
- D Quadrant – Conceptual and risk-taking.

To fully leverage the team, we should assign projects that align with our preferred thinking styles and understand when to stretch our styles to maximize the opportunities through diverse perspectives.

A leadership team can gain immediate benefit from understanding the Whole Brain® thinking by adopting the following:

- Be an agile leader that harnesses team diversity of thought to
  lessen world challenges.
- Assembling or reworking an empowered team based on
  thinking preferences leads to the potential for higher
  performance.
- Increased productivity by leading with the inclusion of
  mind.
- Expanding our view to drive more significant innovation.

- Create a sustainable competitive advantage through attraction, engagement, and retention of high-caliber leadership.

The research by Herrmann found that Whole Brain® teams are 66% more efficient. It is a significant competitive advantage for organizations that embrace the assessment and effectively implement the Whole Brain® Model into their leadership.

An HBDI practitioner will do the following with the assessment results:

- Debrief everyone on the HBDI® Profile and Pair Profile.
- In settings with a workgroup, the debriefing will include a Team Profile.
- Explain the evolution of the Whole Brain® Model and the organizing principle.
- How to apply Whole Brain® Thinking to: communication; teams; clients, decision making and problem-solving; and creative thinking.

The HBDI Adjective Pairs project how everyone on the leadership team would react under pressure. An ideal situation would be to know how various individuals would respond ahead of a crisis and plan accordingly. Therefore, we should assign projects aligned with individuals with the best natural preferences and pressure response combinations. For example, it would not be ideal to have an A Quadrant person doubling down on analytical and logical messaging when a calm C Quadrant person would be better suited to provide participatory and people-oriented updates.

A team profile[4] is possible by combing the individual HBDI results. Knowing where the various executive team members fall on the team profile allows the group to understand how balanced they are in thinking preferences when making collective decisions. The team profile can show potential imbalance before implementing organizational strategies. It may be helpful to add or invite individuals with the missing thinking styles to strengthen group dialogue and critical thinking. Understanding each other's profiles allows for crucial communication with solid points and an understanding of blind spots.

As we continue our exploration of team assessment using personality types, we close out with The Predictive Index (PI). Their talent optimization approach allows organizations to better align their business strategy and talent. The work utilizes a trio of tools. First, the PI Cognitive Assessment™[5] predicts natural learning ability and job performance. Second, the PI Job Assessment™[6] evaluates employees' behavioral traits and cognitive skills. Lastly, the PI Behavioral Assessment™[7] looks at the current hardwiring of employees where placing them in great fits allows them the potential to perform at their highest potential.

Using the outcomes of the PI assessments allows the leadership team to understand themselves more clearly and leverage optimization of the collective group. Setting a stage where team members are comfortable speaking on delicate issues increases team awareness, trust, and communication, promoting greater unity in their work to achieve strategic initiatives. Additionally, the executives have a more significant opportunity for professional development and better health.

Regardless of the chosen approach, all leadership teams can benefit from working through a process to understand better and leverage team dynamics to maximize the opportunity for organizational success. However, it echoes a common theme that it can be challenging and requires a commitment to engage with one another in an environment of trust and caring to achieve an ideal state of executive leadership.

CUTTING THE TAIL

Several years ago, I learned the "cut the tail" concept of change management. Sadly, I do not remember the book title. However, the authors used a bell curve to argue that a small percentage of the employees on the right would embrace organizational change. A small group fighting or sabotaging the improvement plan would be on the left of the curve. The workforce balance would wait to see how things unfold to determine which end of the curve to follow. The concept can also be applied to a leadership team. The authors recommend cutting the left tail to ensure change success. If those on the left are given a just opportunity to participate but are unwilling to adapt to a humanist approach, it may make sense to cut anyone on that side of the curve.

REFINEMENT OF THE "WHY," VISION, MISSION, AND VALUES

During the work to improve the team dynamics, the owner or leader should share their initial work to define the "why," vision, mission, and values. Then, the leadership team should collaborate to refine these essential elements for reaching high levels of organizational success. Next, the leader can walk the group through the evolution of thought that led to the current iterations. Then the team can talk about what was compelling and share insights about what they feel could help enhance them. Ultimately, the objective is to reach a consensus on them and commit to the team's complete buy-in. When sharing them with the balance of the organization's internal and external stakeholders, there must be no outward dissent from the leadership group.

CLOSING COMMENTS

Those responsible for managing a team will generally have tremendous success if they hire appropriately intelligent people and let them do their job, as the Steve Jobs quote suggests. We should also pay it forward to those who desire to become good managers. Modeling appropriate behavior and helping them develop the same skills related to respect, trust, and positivity can ripple throughout an organization.

Ultimately, similar to the suggestion for the leader, it may be beneficial to enlist an outside party to guide the executive team first through individual coaching and to assist in the team-building process. First, the person can smooth the likely difficult conversations. Next, the facilitator can provide new thinking during this organizational evolution. In addition, an outsider's view can help to see opportunities the group may otherwise overlook. Finally, the outsider can be the person who raises the questions that the team may be initially uncomfortable asking one another.

CHAPTER REFLECTION QUESTIONS

Is your leadership team aligned with your "why"?

Does your leadership team have a balance of Executing, Influencing, Relationship Building, and Strategic Building skills (CliftonStrengths)?

Does your leadership team have a balance of Analytical, Experimental, Practical, and Relational thinking styles (Herrmann Brain Dominance Index)?

Do your executives need personal growth and team development to fully embrace humanist commitments to support your plans for transformative change?

Is there a need to justly cut the tail of any executives unable or unwilling to embrace the transformation process?

Is the executive team ready to provide insight further to refine the vision, mission, and values?

How does the executive team create an environment for success now and in the future?

What is the leadership group doing to create a focus on actions that will achieve the organization's mission and vision?

How does the adoption of humanist commitments align with your thoughts on the content of this chapter?

RECOMMENDED READING

Now, Discover Your Strengths: The Revolutionary Gallup Program that Shows You How to Develop Your Unique Talents and Strengths 20th Anniversary Edition (2020) – Marcus Buckingham and Donald O. Clifton – The Free Press

The Whole Brain Business Book: Unlocking the Power of Whole Brain Thinking in Organizations, Teams, and Individuals, 2nd Edition (2015) – Ned Herrmann and Ann Herrmann-Nehdi – McGraw-Hill Education

PHASE 3

DEVELOP INTERNAL OPS

3. Establish robust internal operations that fully support employees' needs to successfully carry out the "why" or mission.

Phase 3 focuses on building overall operations aligned with the humanist commitments from the internal organizational perspective. It begins with selecting the business operating system (BOS) the company will use to develop "a company guidebook that outlines the what, how, when, and why regarding company responsibilities."[1] Chapter 5 begins with a recommendation for a BOS that aligns well with the humanist manufacturing framework. The chapter also includes content on the United Nations Sustainable Development Goals, the benefits of adopting lean manufacturing, and the wisdom of W. Edwards Deming's 14 Points for Management.

The content in Chapters 6-9 shares a wide range of approaches that a manufacturing operation is integrating humanist commitments can adopt. Chapter 6 looks at various ways to conduct product design. Environmentally favorable materials are the emphasis of Chapter 7. A review in Chapter 8 looks at trends impacting manufacturing processes. Phase 3 closes out in Chapter 9, focusing on initiatives companies can integrate to become more sustainable operations.

Essential manufacturing company departments like accounting, customer service, finance, marketing, purchasing, quality, sales, and supply chain are not the focus of this book. However, these will play an essential role in adopting and supporting the transition to becoming a humanist manufacturer.

CHAPTER 5
THE BUSINESS OPERATING SYSTEM

*"Long-term commitment to new learning and new philosophy is
required of any management that seeks transformation. The timid and
the fainthearted, and the people that expect quick results, are doomed
to disappointment."*

—W. Edwards Deming

I have worked on the two extremes of rules philosophy: unwritten and
ever-changing rules, and the other where it seemed likely that a job
instruction existed for wiping one's derriere. Goldilocks would likely
agree that there must be something in between that is "just right."
Eighty percent of the pendulum swing to the side of a clearly defined
and adhered to set of policies, procedures, and job instructions is probably the ideal state. So it might be more or less for a particular operation. However, the 80-20 rule came to mind when picking a number
where eighty percent of the business operating system (BOS) ensures
that things happen seamlessly. In contrast, the other twenty percent
allows the workforce enough flexibility to adapt when meeting stakeholder needs.

What we will explore in this chapter requires much time and

energy. However, when done well, the results exceed the energy needed to make transformative change a reality. The effectiveness of the BOS should lead to standardization across the organization. In addition, the allocation of resources must align with its central "why," vision, and mission. It defines the activities employees can expect while carrying out their various responsibilities. Finally, it drives continuous improvement of the organization. We will explore how the BOS operates similarly to the human body, the B Impact Assessment as an ideal BOS for humanist manufacturers, the integration of United Nations Sustainable Development Goals, and how lean operations allow us to enhance our organizations further.

A BOS ANALOGY

I see the human body having comparable elements to an effective BOS. Each part of the human anatomy depends on all body parts to carry out a defined role, as does an organization count on each employee to meet or exceed the requirements of their position. The brain constantly monitors and adjusts body functions and the external environment through two-way communication to maintain a healthy life. Inputs like oxygen and nutrients should arrive promptly at proper levels. Like a cut, the body responds by clotting the blood to reduce blood flow if harm happens.

Similar actions and reactions are necessary to maintain an efficient and effective production environment, such as the need to respond to and repair a breakdown on a manufacturing line. In addition, manufacturing inputs need to arrive promptly from a highly functional supply chain. The external environment also needs ongoing scanning to monitor potential negative impacts on the organization. Essentially, weakness in any part of the body resembles deficiency anywhere in an organization, where both depend on proper planning and care to maintain them at an optimal state.

B IMPACT ASSESSMENT

Organizations have various frameworks to choose from to implement an internal operating system. The one I have found that most closely aligns with the humanist manufacturing framework is from B Lab. B Lab is "transforming the global economy to benefit all people, communities, and the planet." B Lab is supporting the B Corp movement as a means to offer a concrete, market-based, and scalable solution to our societal challenges.

As a 501(c)3 nonprofit, B Lab (2014) was founded by Jay Cohen Gilbert and Bart Houlahan, who had sold their AND 1 basketball shoe company, and Andrew Kassoy, a former Wall Street private equity investor, who were collectively trying to figure out what was next for them.[1] After evaluating several options and having many conversations with investors, thought leaders, and entrepreneurs, they found the need for two pieces of infrastructure for businesses working to be a force for good. The first was to create a legal framework to protect corporations desiring to make a social and/or public environmental benefit. The second was to develop reasonable standards that distinguish responsible companies from others in the marketplace.

The legal framework[2] ensures that the company can continue to practice its mission through stakeholder governance even after leadership changes, capital raises, or a potential sale. The commitment is to be accountable to all stakeholders. In addition to shareholders, the organization is responsible to the community, customers, the environment, suppliers, and workers. Ultimately, continued protection is in place to create a lasting commitment and accountability to its stakeholders to support an economy that works for everyone.

The resultant standard is the B Impact Assessment[3] (BIA), which measures a company's environmental and social impact. The BIA has five categories with a possible total of 200 points. The following is a brief description[4] of the criteria for each category and a sample BIA question:

1. *Community* – The impact of an organization on their local community relates to initiatives like charitable giving; civic

engagement; cooperative models; diversity, equity, and inclusion; fair trade sourcing, local economic development, and poverty alleviation.

What % of your total cost of materials in the last fiscal year came from underserved suppliers that have received the above capacity-building support?

2. *Customers* – The company supplies quality products and services that ethically address a particular social issue directly or through its customers to improve the social impact of other businesses or organizations.

In what ways do you determine whether the organizations you serve directly support underserved populations?

3. *Environment* – Measurement of a company's environmental impact on the air, biodiversity, climate, land, and water. Additional points are available for organizations that provide products and services with a positive environmental impact.

Which of the following environmental metrics does your company track regarding the environmental impact of your product or service?

4. *Governance* – The company's environmental or social impact, ethics, mission, and transparency; additionally, the ability of the organization to protect the mission and incorporate stakeholders in its decision-making.

How does your company integrate social and environmental performance into decision-making?

5. *Workers* – The contribution to employee well-being related to career development, engagement and satisfaction, financial security, health and safety, and wellness. Furthermore, companies gain additional points to support community members with employment barriers or non-executive ownership of 40% or more.

What percentage of employees on an FTE (Full Time Equivalent) basis are paid at least the equivalent of a living wage for an individual?

Organizations that score 80 or more points upon verification by B Lab can become a Certified B Corporation. B Lab provides several ways to support businesses with benchmarks, standards, and tools for companies that choose to pursue certification. I profile several manufacturers[5] with this certification status in this book, further evidence of the fit between the framework and humanist manufacturing. Furthermore, I plan to work toward achieving this goal for my consulting company.

SUSTAINABLE DEVELOPMENT GOALS

B Lab has further improved its impact potential by integrating the United Nations (UN) Sustainable Development Goals[6] (SDGs) to bring together the Ten Principles of the UN Global Compact with the B Impact Assessment. The 17 SDGs are:

- *Goal 1 - End poverty in all its forms everywhere.*
- *Goal 2 – End hunger, achieve food security and improved nutrition and promote sustainable agriculture.*
- *Goal 3 – Ensure healthy lives and promote well-being for all at all ages.*
- *Goal 4 - Ensure inclusive and equitable quality education and promote lifelong learning opportunities for all.*
- *Goal 5 - Achieve gender equality and empower all women and girls.*
- *Goal 6 - Ensure availability and sustainable management of water and sanitation for all.*
- *Goal 7 - Ensure access to affordable, reliable, sustainable and modern energy for all.*
- *Goal 8 - Promote sustained, inclusive and sustainable economic growth, full and productive employment and decent work for all.*
- *Goal 9 - Build resilient infrastructure, promote inclusive and sustainable industrialization and foster innovation.*
- *Goal 10 - Reduce inequality within and among countries*
- *Goal 11 - Make cities and human settlements inclusive, safe, resilient and sustainable.*

- *Goal 12 - Ensure sustainable consumption and production patterns.*
- *Goal 13 - Take urgent action to combat climate change and its impacts.*
- *Goal 14 - Conserve and sustainably use the oceans, seas and marine resources for sustainable development.*
- *Goal 15 - Protect, restore and promote sustainable use of terrestrial ecosystems, sustainably manage forests, combat desertification, and halt and reverse land degradation and halt biodiversity loss.*
- *Goal 16 - Promote peaceful and inclusive societies for sustainable development, provide access to justice for all and build effective, accountable and inclusive institutions at all levels.*
- *Goal 17 - Strengthen the means of implementation and revitalize the Global Partnership for Sustainable Development.*

The SDG Action Manager is a free web-based impact management solution built through B Lab and the United Nations Global Impact collaboration. The SDG Action Manager allows businesses to focus on their organization's individual SDG goals of importance. This tool guides them toward internal reflection and the development of specific actions. Several of the UN SDGs align well with the humanist commitments and work to achieve the vision of "The manufacturing industry allows each citizen of the world an opportunity to meet at a minimum their needs for just and healthy lives, with a full opportunity to achieve their highest potential."

LEAN MANUFACTURING

In the early 1990s, I worked for Michigan Automotive Compressor, Inc., a joint venture of Toyota Industries Corporation and Denso, in Parma, MI. The manufacturing operation fully integrated the Toyota Production System (TPS). It was not a good match for me personally and professionally at that point in my career. I did not fully appreciate the "system" I was immersed in while working at the company. Many years later, when learning more about the history and philosophies of TPS, I fully understood what I was fortunate to have experienced. I often wished that my other employers would have adopted lean manufacturing using the advice of Taiichi Ohno, the founder of TPS, of "doing it all the way."

Lean focuses on eliminating waste, aligning well with the humanist manufacturing framework. An eighth waste[7] added by some to the original seven from Tachi Ohno is that of unused talent. When we underutilize employee skills, we lessen their potential to make a more significant positive impact.

Charles Intrieri[8] did an excellent job of concisely identifying an overview of TPS (Italicized words are his original content):

1. Base your management decisions on a long-term philosophy, even at the expense of short-term financial goals.
The humanist manufacturing operation will align with this principle, focusing on a long-term commitment to human well-being.

2. Create continuous process flow to bring problems to the surface.
In an ideal TPS system, you would have zero inventory on hand from the initial input to the final output for every production part manufactured in your operation. One-piece flow means that each process takes the component from the previous operation to complete the next process step. As a result, identifying a defect occurs immediately, eliminating more significant numbers that may require rework or disposal in a conventional batch production system.

3. Use "Pull" system to avoid overproduction.
Only producing the minimum volume to meet customer needs eliminates the potential for later disposal of obsolete products.

4. Level out the workload (heijunka). ("Work like a tortoise, not the hare").
The objective is a production pace that produces products at optimal efficiency.

5. Build a culture of stopping to fix problems, to get quality right at the first time.
Gone are the days of continuing to keep a production line going at all costs. Instead, the norm should immediately stop production and eliminate that issue upon recognizing a problem.

6. Standardized tasks are the foundation for continuous improvements and employee empowerment.
In addition, standardization of a continually improving process allows for more efficient production.

7. Use Visual Control so no problems are hidden.
Strong organizations create an environment where the system breakdown is the issue and not the workforce allowing for comfort in raising production issues upon identification.

8. Use only reliable, thoroughly tested technology that serves your people and process.
Innovation is necessary as companies evolve. However, innovation should follow a development process that enhances operators' work to meet customer requirements.

9. Grow leaders who thoroughly understand the work, live philosophy and teach it to others.
Leadership development at all levels of the organization is essential to supporting the needs of employees to be their best selves.

10. Develop exceptional people and teams who follow your company's philosophy.
Innovative companies understand the value of continual development to maximize the full potential of each employee and, collectively, the entire workforce.

11. Respect your extended network of partners and suppliers by challenging them and helping them improve.

Likewise, *the* organization's external stakeholders are an essential element of the company and should receive the same level of support to achieve their full potential.

12. Go to Gemba and see for yourself to thoroughly understand the situation (Genchi Genbutsu).
Walking in the shoes of those doing the work is the only way to comprehend what is occurring.

13. Make decisions slowly by consensus (use cross-functional teams), thoroughly considering all options; implement decisions rapidly.
Putting in the upfront work to thoroughly vet improvements leads to more robust implementation.

14. Become a learning organization through relentless reflection (Hansei) and continuous improvements (Kaizen).
We must develop a lifelong learning mindset where evaluating our past performance allows for enhancing future work. Furthermore, we need to continually monitor innovation that occurs beyond the walls of our factories, both within our industry and in other sectors.

TPS aligns well with net-zero initiatives because eliminating waste is the end goal. The objective is to create a continuous improvement mindset where the organization is continually becoming more efficient and effective.

DEMING'S APPROACH TO THRIVING AND SYSTEMATIC FOCUS

Dr. W. Edwards Deming developed 14 Points for Management, which are as relevant and essential to creating a systems perspective today as when he designed them in his 1982 book *Out of the Crisis*.[9] Deming's comprehensive theory of management is a model of wisdom and simplicity consisting of his 14 points:

1. *Create constancy of purpose toward improvement of product and service, with the aim to become competitive and to stay in business, and to provide jobs.*
2. *Adopt the new philosophy. We are in a new economic age. Western management must awaken to the challenge, must learn their responsibilities, and take on leadership for change.*
3. *Cease dependence on inspection to achieve quality. Eliminate the need for inspection on a mass basis by building quality into the product in the first place.*
4. *End the practice of awarding business on the basis of price tag. Instead, minimize total cost. Move towards a single supplier for any one item, on a long-term relationship of loyalty and trust.*
5. *Improve constantly and forever the system of production and service, to improve quality and productivity, and thus constantly decrease costs.*
6. *Institute training on the job.*
7. *Institute leadership. The aim of supervision should be to help people and machines and gadgets to do a better job. Supervision of management is in need of an overhaul, as well as supervision of production workers.*
8. *Drive out fear, so that everyone may work effectively for the company.*
9. *Break down barriers between departments. People in research, design, sales, and production must work as a team, to foresee problems of production and in use that may be encountered with the product or service.*
10. *Eliminate slogans, exhortations, and targets for the workforce asking for zero defects and new levels of productivity. Such exhortations only create adversarial relationships, as the bulk of the causes of low quality and low productivity belong to the system and thus lie beyond the power of the workforce.*
11. *a) Eliminate work standards (quotas) on the factory floor. Substitute leadership. b) Eliminate management by objective. Eliminate management by numbers, numerical goals. Substitute leadership.*

12. *a) Remove barriers that rob the hourly paid worker of his right to pride in workmanship. The responsibility of supervisors must be changed from sheer numbers to quality. b) Remove barriers that rob people in management and engineering of their right to pride in workmanship. This means, inter alia, abolishment of the annual or merit rating and management by objective.*

13. *Institute a vigorous program of education and self-improvement.*

14. *Put everybody in the company to work to accomplish the transformation. The transformation is everybody's job.*

He further articulated a System of Profound Knowledge in the 1980s and 1990s, resulting in a highly integrated framework for leaders who can use thought and action to transform an organization. The successful integration of these principles leads to a thriving and systematic focus organization. While he may not have had humanist commitments in mind when developing his work, they align with his approach to realizing an ideal manufacturing state. Therefore, the Deming Points for Management should be integral in developing your BOS from my perspective.

CLOSING COMMENTS

Organizations must develop and implement a BOS with full integration. There is no easy answer to which business operating system is ideal for your company. Each organization must compare customer requirements and its "why," vision, mission, and values to determine the best one to adopt. However, holistically adopting the B Impact Assessment, lean manufacturing, and Deming's points are ideal for maximizing an organization's ability to generate more significant environmental and social impacts while enhancing the financial bottom line—a recurring theme throughout the book.

CHAPTER REFLECTION QUESTIONS

Is a BOS in place that:

- Effectively and efficiently communicates with internal and external stakeholders?
- Monitors performance management?
- Ensures process standardization?
- Increase organizational capability through improvement management?
- Results in delivering products and services that meet customer requirements while protecting the environment and society?
- Provides all stakeholders a safe working environment?

What are your organizational leadership structure and governance structure?

What structures and mechanisms make up your organization's leadership system?

As appropriate, what are the reporting relationships among your governance board, senior leaders, and parent organization?

How does the adoption of humanist commitments align with your thoughts on the content of this chapter?

RECOMMENDED READING

Out of the Crisis (2018) – W. Edwards Deming – The MIT Press

The B Corp Handbook, Second Edition: How You Can Use Business as a Force for Good (2019) – Ryan Honeyman and Tiffiany Jana – Berrett-Koehler Publishers, Inc.

The Goal: A Process of Ongoing Improvement (2014) – Eliyahu M. Goldratt and Jeff Cox – North River Press

The Toyota Way: 14 Management Principles from the World's Greatest Manufacturer (2020) – Jeffrey Liker – McGraw-Hill

CHAPTER 6
PRODUCT DESIGN

*"The ultimate test of man's conscience may be his willingness to
sacrifice something today for future generations whose words of thanks
will not be heard."*

—GAYLORD NELSON

World War II was a terrible war that impacted the world in many
devastating ways. Unfortunately, one less-recognized impact is the
emergence of the plastics era,[1] due to war production consuming most
of the available aluminum, copper, steel, and zinc. Another ultimately
undesirable environmental impact was the rise of design for dispos-
ability. A simple example was the shift from returnable glass bottles to
first aluminum, then the disposable glass bottle, and eventually, PET
plastic became the norm. Unfortunately, in recent decades, the primary
approach to design has led to a hyper-disposable[2] world. Fortunately,
this chapter will explore more sustainable designs that continue to
evolve to lessen or eliminate past practices' negative environmental
and social impacts.

CIRCULAR DESIGN

A name synonymous with Swiss innovation is Albin Kälin. He is the CEO of the Environmental Protection Encouragement Agency[3] (EPEA) in Switzerland. His pioneering work in ecological and sustainable manufacturing began as the president of a textile mill. His work focuses on sustainable development's Cradle to Cradle® (C2C) concept.

Kälin's willingness to innovate and his environmental ideology began as the managing director of Rohner Textil from 1981-to 2004. The renowned high-end upholstery manufacturer faced traditional issues in the textile industry, including Asian competition and productivity and waste emissions issues. Kälin had the additional problems of a historic early-1900s factory and noise sensitivity by locals to the milling machines. His work caught the attention of Steelcase Corporation, which was looking for environmentally responsible fabrics. A Steelcase VP introduced Kälin to green designer Will McDonough.

Kälin states[4] that industry has historically used natural resources as an unlimited supply with little regard for waste. However, the reality has set in as the economy has become global. A linear approach from the cradle to the grave is unsustainable, with a need to design products differently. Consumers and the environment are pressuring companies to move from the cradle to the grave approach to C2C. The ideal state will be at the end of product life to either biodegrade or reuse in a new product.

A product design collaboration between cyclos-HTP, System Deutschland, and EPEA Switzerland developed laundry packaging using the C2C model. The designers consulted with a wide range of expertise to revisit the pouch design resulting in complete waste at the end of product use. Plastics can include up to five thousand different substances, and breakdown occurs with plastics exposure to heat, sunlight, and water. A further complication comes in multi-layer packaging design. The objective of a C2C-certified design is that it be completely recyclable. The Swiss group developed an equivalent product with the same capabilities as the original rigid plastic container, using 30 percent less material, easily recyclable, and without degrading product quality.

Kälin's organization, EPEA, is focused on helping business partners and customers to develop a circular economy through C2C design. EPEA[5] uses its 30 years of experience to create and innovate buildings for entire urban areas and processes and products. The services they provide are for C2C design of:

- Buildings,
- Business transformation,
- Cities and infrastructure, and
- Industry products.

The main objective of this work is to develop an outcome that is "beneficial to humans."

CRADLE-TO-CRADLE DESIGN

The work of Will McDonough and Michael Braungart to develop the Cradle to Cradle[6] (C2C) methodology is cyclical with two classifications: biological cycle and technological cycle. Those that are biological are naturally biodegradable. Technological are chemicals, metals, and oil-based materials that can be reused or recycled in a closed system that produces equal or better quality. C2C[7] is a practical, innovative, and quality design that is chemically safe and recyclable. The concept results in safe and potentially ongoing reuse of materials and nutrients cycles.

The linear approach to the consumption of world resources is not a sustainable long-term approach. As collective stakeholders, we must work quickly to have more designers practice the C2C methodology. Our current disposable economy negatively impacts the poor while the wealthiest few become richer, at times at the expense of others. We need to shift quickly to become better stewards of our natural resources.

Cradle to Cradle: Remaking the Way We Make Things[8] is a book by McDonough and Braungart that provides an overview of C2C written by those who developed the methodology. The content integrates design and science that helps the reader understand the benefits to society. One of many TED talks by McDonough, *Cradle to Cradle Design*,[9] provides an additional opportunity to learn more about the benefits of adopting C2C.

BIOMIMICRY

Janine Benyus[10] was the co-founder of the world's first bio-inspired consultancy. What was initially named the Biomimicry Guild is now Biomimicry 3.8, a tribute to the 3.8 billion years of the earth's life. The organization focuses on nature's sustainable design to inspire manufactured designs replicating the natural world. The goal is a new way of living through biomimicry design to meet sustainability challenges through processes, products, and systems mimicking nature's wisdom.

An article[11] on the topic shares ten examples of manufacturers using biomimicry design. In addition, using nature's laboratory led to the potential inspiration of:

1. van der Waals forces create adhesion on the feet of geckos through millions of tiny hairs on their feet, allowing them to scale a wide variety of surfaces and orientations with ease. The Menrva research lab at Simon Fraser University uses this discovery to adhere robots to any surface on earth and in space.
2. Kingfisher divers inspired Western Japan Railway's full-speed bullet train design that exceeds 200 mph. The birdwatcher and chief engineer Eiji Nakatsu used the ability of this bird to move through the elements without disturbance to eliminate the issues associated with high-speed travel.
3. Self-cleaning paint utilizes the "lotus effect" of the lotus leaf. The plant has an air cushion effect that blocks the adherence of mildew, mold, and other dingy culprits from attaching to its leaves.

4. Butterflies that exhibit color characteristics of illuminance, brightness, and vibrance are the inspiration for designing natural paint colors to replace those that use dyes, toxins, and artificial illumination.
5. Qualcomm's Mirasol technologies also mimic the butterfly characteristics in their various display screens.
6. A cement manufacturer of a product as flexible as a rubber hose and as strong as steel led a Parker Hannifin design to replicate snakeskins' scales with a series of interlocking ceramic hexagons.
7. Airbus has a series of biomimicry design projects utilizing the northern gannet capability to use its beak as a sensor to adjust wing shape in response to gust loads.
8. A fan manufacturer, WhalePower, replicates the bumps on the humpback whale that reduce drag and noise in producing industrial fans and power-generating wind turbines.
9. Knowledge gained from the study of termite mounds in Africa that can maintain a stable internal temperature, despite the extremes of heat and cold, is the basis for designing the HVAC system in the Eastgate Building in Harare, Zimbabwe using 90% less energy for ventilation than conventional buildings.
10. The maximum strength of tree fibers guides the design of car frames that are lighter and safer than ever.

The giant research and design lab of 3.8 billion years of evolution is a wealth of knowledge to inform the work of designers and manufacturers.

The newest 3D printers, otherwise known as additive manufacturing, are leading a revolution in design possibilities that were not possible with existing technologies—coupling this emerging processing potential with innovative materials like graphene results in lightweight products ten times stronger than steel. In addition, the intricacies of biomimicry designs[12] possible with 3D are copying nature to restore fertility in mice, foam ink printing, lattice structures in footwear, and 3D printed armor.

Using C2C and biomimicry methodologies will lead to more sustainable designs. Additional design considerations are material selection and processing needs. Cost minimization, economics, reduction of material waste, recyclability or reuse, and process energy consumption are essential details that also need additional attention. Ultimately, the final product should do no environmental or social harm throughout its life.

SURFACE ENGINEERING

Gone are the days when we accept a material's standalone properties. An example is that an engineer can design a product that provides the needed structural strength while adding a coating protecting it from an operating environment's abuse through surface engineering. The discipline of surface engineering involves changing the exterior layer's properties to enhance performance. Options include adhesion, corrosion resistance, friction reduction, hardness, impact resistance, porosity, processing factors, and wear resistance.

Imagine a world where cars rusted prematurely. All product finishes were the dull, muddy colors of raw materials. One with bacteria growing in hospital walls. Jets that frequently crash due to stress fractures in turbine blades. Surface engineering benefits include rust-resistant metal coatings, durable paint finishes for vehicles and appliances, anti-bacterial coatings for medical facilities, and stress-resistant surface treatment for aerospace components. A blog post[13] by the European Committee for Surface Treatment shares why surface engineering is essential. If I have convinced you that we need surface engineering, it would be good to understand the processes.

A.S. Khanna explains[14] three surface engineering processes: the first is changing the surface without altering the material chemistry. The change involves altering metallurgy or surface texture through electromechanical etching, laser engraving, mechanical, or thermal means. A second approach is to change the surface through chemistry. New chemical elements are diffused into the original surface to become an enhanced, modified surface. The final option included surface modification. The outside layer receives a manufacturing surface coating of additional material. Next, we will review a process to help determine the ideal surface engineering solution.

The Surface Engineering Alloy Company provides a process[15] to surface engineering solutions. The initial step is to identify the components' wear problems, including abrasion, adhesion, erosion, and surface fatigue. Next, an engineer will define the best application and process to resolve the issue depending on the identified problem. For each customer, customized selection occurs to optimize material performance. Next, they determine the proper application, measurement criteria, and performance testing. The subsequent phase is to validate the product or service with the client. The final determination of success is to monitor customer satisfaction and, if necessary, reevaluate the process to adjust accordingly. While their company has developed a method, we will further expand our understanding of the many disciplines and areas using surface engineering in materials design.

INTERDISCIPLINARY COLLABORATIVE RESEARCH

The Surface Engineering Research Center[16] (SERC) collaborates with three South Dakota universities working across five academic disciplines from three areas of expertise: advanced characterization, advanced materials and manufacturing, and surface engineering technology. Their work involves biomedical applications, including antimicrobial implant coatings, drug-eluting implant coatings, and wear-resistant surfaces for load-bearing implants. In addition, they develop corrosion and wear-resistant coatings and super-hydrophobic and icephobic coatings in defense, energy, and environmental applications. Their research around advanced materials includes advanced composites, ceramics, carbon NTs, graphene, metals, and polymers. The characterization focuses on composition and structure, hardness and elastic modulus, porosity, surface roughness, wear and corrosion, and wettability. Lastly, they advance the process technologies of anodic oxidation, cold spray, functionalized carboxylate deposition, laser deposition, nanoparticle spray, and vapor deposition.

CLOSING COMMENTS

The combination of environmentally and socially friendly design leads to the exciting potential to meet consumer needs in a manner that benefits the world. Moving from a recent historical approach of using products for minutes that exist as waste, in some cases harming society for centuries, must become an obsolete practice. Adopting more responsible design practices is also an opportunity to reduce the current overconsumption of diminishing world resources.

CHAPTER REFLECTION QUESTIONS

Are criteria for responsible design developed and followed?

Economic
- Disposal cost?
- Initial cost?
- Maintenance cost?

Environmental
- Energy savings?
- Potential for recycling and reuse?
- Raw materials extraction?

Social
- Esthetics?
- Health and safety?
- Operational life?
- Technical?
- Life expectancy?
- Maintainability?
- Resistance to decay?

How does the adoption of humanist commitments align with your thoughts on the content of this chapter?

RECOMMENDED READING

Biomimicry: Innovation Inspired by Nature (2002) – Janine Benyus – Perennial

Cradle to Cradle: Remaking the Way We Make Things (2002) – Will McDonough and Michael Braungart – North Point Press

Cradle-to-Cradle Design: Creating Healthy Emissions — A Strategy for Eco-Effective Product and System Design (2007) – Michael Braungart, William McDonough, Albin Kälin, and Andrew Bollinger – Journal of Cleaner Production

Green Design and Manufacturing for Sustainability (2016) – Nand K. Jha – CRC Press

CHAPTER 7
MATERIALS SELECTION

*"Infinite growth of material consumption in a finite world
is an impossibility."*

— E. F. SCHUMACHER

The original 4 M manufacturing categories in the Cause-Effect Diagram created by Kaoru Ishikawa included materials. This production element's importance remains. The average cost of raw materials for most automotive components we produced at my former employers was 65-70% of the total cost. Additionally, we are experiencing significant changes in the type and structures of materials now available. The focus of this chapter is a brief overview of a sample of emerging material applications.

ADVANCING TO THE CREATION AGE

James Arbib and Tony Seba wrote *Rethinking Humanity: Five Foundational Sector Disruptions, the Lifecycle of Civilizations, and the Coming Age of Freedom.*[1] They provide examples of ways manufacturing companies can align their work by addressing various societal and environmental issues described as the Creation Age. An example is a forecasted move from the extraction of materials to resource creation. With an impressive track record of future trends, they predict that materials costs will drop by 10X, a realization of a 90% reduction of natural resources, and there will be 100% less waste.

They see a Creation Age where the production model involves self-replicating building blocks of nature. These building blocks will include seed stocks of metals, leading to locally abundant resources supporting self-sufficient communities. Digital knowledge will have significant global flows, massive production of local goods, and limited global flow of goods. The competition for resources will diminish as seed stocks grow, leading to low costs, high efficiencies, and near-zero waste.

GOING LIGHTWEIGHT

Avi Reichental, in a blog post,[2] makes a statement that lightweighting is "making something less heavy." He further shares that this is emerging as a critical concern for the automotive and transportation industries. A typical approach is usually a material substitution or reduction. An automotive industry example that comes to mind is Ford introducing a military-grade aluminum-alloy body F-150 pickup truck. Some may remember the Chevrolet Silverado advertisements showing their high-strength steel holding up better when dropping concrete blocks into the bed of their pickup versus that of the aluminum body Ford. The result was minor scratches and dents in the Chevy bed, while the Ford aluminum bed experienced severe damage. Chevy's ad suggested that bed durability was more important than fuel economy gains from a Ford truck that was 700 pounds lighter. But, then, one might ask why Ford would build an aluminum truck body?

The evolution of lightweighting is related to the 2025 CAFE standards. A March 31, 2020, news release[3] announced a change of 5% to 1.5% in yearly improvement in CAFE and CO_2 emissions for the 2021-2026 model years. Since CAFE and CO_2 emissions are likely to continue as global concerns, there will be a market need to advance new materials technologies.

Bill Koenig, the senior editor at SME Media, indicates that lightweighting is entering a new phase. The expected rush to replace steel with aluminum is transitioning to a mix of materials that will differ across vehicle types. Ultimately the expectation is that composite materials are the long-term answer. However, the retired president of the Center of Automotive Research (CAR), Jay Baron, states that weight and strength are only part of the equation where cost, vibration, and stiffness need to be adequately considered from a design perspective. While not included in the article, developing the production processes required to manufacture composites and post-purchase needs to consider factors like body repair after a vehicle crash is critical. These are just a few of the many actions needed to shift from current vehicle designs to those that will emerge in the future. We will now transition to a familiar path of new technology adoption occurring first with luxury vehicles.

Fitzgerald and Mazumdar of Lucintel presented[4] at the 2018 Composites Europe industry meeting on the future of lightweight technologies. They predicted a compound annual growth rate (CAGR) of 5% in global lightweight materials demand. Market estimates for global composites will reach $28 billion by 2025 with a similar 5% CAGR. The momentum is gaining with a logical initial adoption in high-end vehicles built by OEMs, including Audi, BMW, Ferrari, and Lamborghini. Initial uses include bumpers, c-pillars, chassis, fenders, floor panels, hoods, roofs, and tailgates.

The presentation included a case study on BWM's use of carbon composites. Benefits included the expected weight savings and improved mileage. For example, the BMW i3 has 9% greater MPGe than Nissan Leaf and 19% greater than Tesla Model S. The i3 weight was 19% less than the Leaf and 43% lighter than the Model S. The price comparison was an i3 at about $42,000 with the Leaf at $30,000 and the Model S at $70,000.

The Chevy vs. Ford example shows the need to adapt materials to the vehicle owner's needs. My experience is that most pickup owners never haul anything beyond occasional groceries in their truck bed, so the concrete blocks are probably not an issue. If so, they could spend $120 to buy a bed liner. On the other hand, someone who works a ranch or in the construction industry might want to go with a Chevy. The trickle-down of materials advancement to lower-cost models will be interesting to see. We can expect similar results with an adaptive cruise control system with lane-centering assist and automated emergency braking with pedestrian detection, which were once available on high-end vehicles and are now regularly available on lower-end cars.

USING GRAPHENE TO ADVANCE THE WORLD

Graphenea CEO Jesus de la Fuente describes graphene[5] as a tightly bound hexagonal lattice in a single honeycomb layer of carbon atoms. Stacking these in multiple layers is based on graphite, 100-300 times stronger than steel. At one atom thick, graphene is the thinnest and lightest material known to man. Graphene improves batteries' charge rate, capacity, and longevity. Other applications include all-solid-state graphene-based supercapacitors, radio frequency (RF) flexible electronics, self-powered triboelectric sensors, strain sensors, wearable touch panels, and touchscreens for mobile devices and wristwatches that are robust and flexible. The evolution of material development is taking electronics to the next level.

Researchers[6] in several major global cities are developing new building blocks using graphene for next-level electronics. Their development, spintronics, transports graphene and two-dimensional (2D) materials to build this form of advanced technology. Spintronics at the nanoscale is an alternative to nanoelectronics. The potential outcome is spin-based memories and transistors for phones and tablets - a promising technology in the automotive industry and hard disk drive reading heads for laptops and personal computers. These leading applications are setting the stage for additional growth.

Dr. Richard Collins shares[7] that graphene use will exceed $300 million in the next decade, per IDTechEx analysts. The smartphone industry has purchased the most graphene to date. Other expected markets include concrete enhancement, lightweight composite structures, lithium-ion batteries, offshore wind turbines, and supercapacitors. While success is not guaranteed, fundamental understandings are emerging of the value of graphene for a wide variety of industry sectors. In addition, the success in graphene applications has led scientists to explore the development of other 2D materials.

Professors Geim and Novoselov experimented[8] with graphite and sticky tape, which resulted in a single-atom-thick layer's exfoliation, which led to graphene discovery. Their discovery resulted in their receipt of the Nobel Prize in 2010. Exploring opportunities to use this material led to creating 2D versions that are flexible and stretchable with excellent electronic properties. The success in 2D material using graphene has led to other stanene types for a phase transition to superconductivity. In addition, the germanium used for the earliest transistors is now replacing silicone for mass production. Further excitement builds as researchers move from 2D to 3D forms that will significantly expand graphene applications.

Research[9] in the Centre for Additive Manufacturing at the University of Nottingham is advancing 3D graphene printing for electronic devices. They replace single-layer graphene used in 2D metal-semiconductor contact materials with tiny flakes of graphene deposited in inks in multiple layers leading to 3D forms. The printed layers are an atom thick but centimeters across to control light and electricity with complex devices—the beginning stages of next-level use of this advanced material.

The content on this topic barely touches on the implications of this advanced material. The scientific detail level is also minimal, given the highly technical nature of graphene to develop significantly advanced 2D and 3D structures. Most of us will not work with materials of this type soon. However, further refinement of processes will emerge as a leading use material in various applications to advance multiple industry sectors.

ADVANCED COMPOSITES AS A BETTER COMBINATION OF MATERIALS

We continue to focus on materials with a look at advanced composites. A Medium article[10] describes composites as combining multiple materials that provide performance or strength that is impossible with a single material. Performance elements possible with composites include lighter weights in highly durable products. In addition, they are adapting designs to meet specific strength criteria and flexibilities. Additional properties are resistance to corrosion and fatigue in composites using organic and inorganic materials. While advanced composites are emerging, composites date back centuries.

Per Advanced Composites, the ancient Ming Dynasty was an early known culture to use composite construction.[11] Manchu artisans developed composite bows using inlaid bone and ligament in bamboo and wood capable of higher projectile speeds through greater draw weight. Over the years, the evolution of composite materials includes ceramics, concrete (used in ancient Rome), cultured marble, textiles, and laminated woods. As different materials and manufacturing processes have emerged, composites' sophistication has advanced significantly to include various construction forms through creative engineering design.

Campbell writes in *Structural Composite Materials*[12] about various forms of composite materials. Two primary reinforcement types are continuous and discontinuous. Continuous examples include unidirectional, woven, and filament wound. The discontinuous versions have chopped and mat fibers. Random short fibers provide the least amount of strength and the most flexibility. Random-aligned composites are stronger with medium elasticity, and aligned fibers have greater rigidity. As fiber volume increases, the strength will increase to a specific volume percentage level regardless of form.

RESEARCH ADVANCES

A Textile World article[13] focuses on using advanced composites to build a clean energy economy. Fiber-reinforced polymers can reduce emissions and improve transportation efficiency with high-strength-to-weight ratios in high-performance products. The Institute for Advanced Composites Manufacturing Innovation (IACMI)[14] accelerates advanced composites' development in focus areas, including materials and processes, modeling and simulation, compressed gas storage, wind technologies, and vehicles. The work is enhancing improved performance in carbon fiber technologies. Other gains include faster cycle times in additives and intermediates, innovative reinforcements, reduced embodied energy, integrated features, and cost reductions. While advancing in this material area, their capabilities are likely less than those of the National Aerospace and Science Administration (NASA).

NASA[15] is taking advanced composites to new heights, literally and figuratively, with state-of-the-art ultra-high-strength fibers. The available blends include nanoparticle, polymer, and polymer-fiber blends. The benefits are enhanced strength, increased material lifetime, damage resistance, and resilient materials ideal for automotive, energy, industrial, and marine applications. Initially developed to reduce manufacturing costs and improve fuel economy, other industries adapt the materials in new ways.

The names of just a few of many material advanced composites examples include 1) nanomaterials that are easier to process while also more formidable and resistant, 2) niobium-titanium titride thin film coating used as a mid-to-far infrared absorber at cryogenic temperatures that simultaneously acts as a high pass filter, 3) resin transfer molding 370 resin for high-temperature applications using a revolutionary solvent-free process, and 4) specular coatings for lightweight mirrors or reflectors. In addition, organizations interested in applying them for their production can license them with NASA, an opportunity to take advantage of some of our tax dollars.

There will be an ongoing integration of advanced composites across all industries. As processes are further optimized and overall costs come down, consumers will benefit through increased safety and decreased fuel costs in various transportation modes—more efficient power generation reduces energy production costs. Additionally, there will also be a net environmental improvement. We should evaluate how advanced composites impact our specific industries and develop an integration plan viable for an organization's environmental, financial, and social elements.

CLOSING COMMENTS

The combination of environmentally and socially friendly designs using ever-advancing materials leads to the exciting potential to meet world needs in a manner that benefits society. The materials from this chapter are a small representation of advances that will continue to emerge. Using a more intelligent approach to materials selection is necessary as current business practices consume natural resources at an unsustainable long-term rate. In particular, as the global population grows, more people are looking to live lives similar to those of the wealthy members of society.

CHAPTER REFLECTION QUESTIONS

Are criteria for responsible design developed and followed?

Economic
- Disposal cost?
- Initial cost?
- Maintenance cost?

Environmental
- Energy savings?
- Potential for recycling and reuse?
- Raw materials extraction?

Social
- Esthetics?
- Health and safety?
- Operational life?
- Technical?
- Life expectancy?
- Maintainability?
- Resistance to decay?

How does the adoption of humanist commitments align with your thoughts on the content of this chapter?

RECOMMENDED READING

Green and Sustainable Manufacturing of Advanced Material (2015) – Editors: Mrityunjay Singh, Tatsuki Ohji, and Rajiv Asthana – Elsevier Inc.

Handbook of Sustainable Polymers for Additive Manufacturing (2022) – Antonio Paesano – CRC Press

Material Value: More Sustainable, Less Wasteful Manufacturing of Everything from Cell Phones to Cleaning Products (2019) – Julia L. F. Goldstein – Bebo Press

Rethinking Humanity: Five Foundational Sector Disruptions, the Lifecycle of Civilizations, and the Coming Age of Freedom (2020) – James Arbib & Tony Seba – RethinkX

CHAPTER 8
PROCESSES

"The real problem is not whether machines think but whether men do."

—B. F. Skinner

The manufacturing industry is seeing similar technological advances that will significantly alter the standard production processes of the past. Additive manufacturing provides adaptability and flexibility previously unseen as one-off complex 3-D products are suddenly possible in a growing variety of material types. Significant reduction in energy consumption and environmental impact is possible as the Industrial Internet of Things (IIoT) optimizes production operations. Employees work in safer conditions, and there is a potential improvement in employee health with the integration of cobots that produce the product in concert with them. The total lifetime manufacturing cost decreases as the shift from production lines for a specific product goes away. Waste of all types is the result of enhanced manufacturing process development.

Evidence of what Seba and Arbib are predicting[1] for processes is already progressing with significant advances in 3D printing, artificial intelligence, and robotics used to create distributed modular production. As a result, many less desirable manufacturing jobs will disappear as clean rooms with 3D printers replace foundries, artificial intelligence addresses quality concerns, and advanced robotics supports production lines. The authors call this the "fastest, deepest, most consequential transformation of human civilization in history," which goes far beyond what others defined as the Fourth Industrial Revolution.

THE INDUSTRY 4.0 EVOLUTION

The days of dark and dingy plants with smokestacks billowing pollution, using uneducated employees like disposable assets, is already mostly a historical approach to manufacturing. The general perception of the industry has already taken significant steps toward meaningful employment opportunities. However, soon the sector will have scientists developing seed stocks, highly skilled technicians, and engineers working with artificial intelligence (AI) and robotics. These plants will significantly improve social and environmental results to entice the next generation of the workforce to accept jobs of significant purpose. Industry 4.0, including the advanced technologies of additive manufacturing, automation, cobots, Industrial Internet of Things (IIoT), and robotics, is a current shift in manufacturing that all plant operations must adapt to remain competitive in the global market.

The "method" used to produce products is an important consideration that has only grown in significance with increasingly sophisticated emerging technologies. Technological advances will continue to alter the manufacturing industry in exciting ways. Additionally, more sophisticated processes allow for the opportunity to produce products that lessen waste and improve the opportunity for jobs with higher pay that will enhance the environmental and social aspects of manufacturing. The first method we will explore is additive manufacturing, also known as 3D printing.

ADDITIVE MANUFACTURING

In the mid-1980s, Charles W. Hull built the first 3D printer[2] using stereolithography. The object would be formed in multiple thin layers by the laser using an ultraviolet-sensitive photopolymer guided by a Computer-Aided Design (CAD) or Computer-Aided Manufacturing (CAM) file. Many have seen the crude 3D printed objects in the earliest iterations of this process. A variety of other 3D technology forms have included fused deposition modeling (FDM), digital light projector (DLP), multi-jet modeling, selective laser sintering (SLS), and electron beam melting (EBM). We will now skip ahead to the current 3D printing that is becoming better known as additive manufacturing.

According to a McKinsey & Company article, plastics and metals are currently the most common materials.[3] Products manufactured with a wide variety of new plastics use processes to include fused deposition modeling (FDM), selective laser sintering (SLS), and stereolithography (SLA). Component production using metals is laser metal deposition (LMD) and direct metal laser spraying (DMLS). New material advances include paper, wood, ceramics, glass, cement, graphene, and living cells. Industries advancing this technology are wide-ranging. We will next review examples tied to manufacturing.

McKinsey's additional article[4] predicts additive manufacturing growth to $10 billion in the 2030-to-2035-time range. An expected shift will move from experimental use to the high-end metals market in five to ten years due to decreased lead times and lower production costs. The reduction from many processing steps to three: metal production, powder production, and product printing. Additional benefits include lower small-batch prices, consistent quality, reduced waste, improved geometries, and enhanced mechanical properties.

The Plastics Machinery[5] magazine predicts that additive manufacturing will result in a location-of-use production model. Product needs vary across countries. This technology can shift supply chains from a "one size fits all" approach to one delivered by local employees that understand their language, culture, and industry requirements. The article includes several examples of success with localized manufacturing, including Nordson, making several acquisitions to create a global company serving local markets. The entrepreneurs who optimize additive manufacturing will meet a wide variety of community needs and, more importantly, keep local wealth within them.

Ben-Ner and Siemsen[6] also see localized production causing a drastic change in the manufacturing industry by mid-century. They argue that supply chains will shrink as production shifts from mega factories to mini-local operations. The transformation will also change the employee requirements from narrow disciplines to a hybrid position that combines sales, consulting, engineering, production, and service skills necessary to serve the local market. UPS sees the negative impact of reduced supply chains on its delivery business and is exploring the development of additive manufacturing operations worldwide. The mega to mini transition is possible as the former benefit of large volumes leading to per piece cost reductions in traditional manufacturing disappears as additive manufacturing has relatively constant per piece costs, regardless of volume. Ongoing enhancement of additive technologies will continue to shrink per piece costs.

Despite the many issues the US is experiencing with COVID-19, racial unrest, political division, unemployment, and much more, we see a positive trend of significant manufacturing advances. The ability to shift production to a localized point of use consumption through additive manufacturing is an exciting period in the industry's history. I expect this production method to have an additional benefit of significant positive environmental, financial, and social impacts on our communities.

THE INTERNET OF THINGS

The Internet of Things (IoT) is another of the latest buzzwords in manufacturing. According to the American Society of Quality research, manufacturers who have successfully adopted this technology have enjoyed 82% increased efficiency, 49% fewer product defects, and 45% increased customer satisfaction. So if you are looking for more significant data collection, increased analysis, greater operations insight, and greater efficiencies, you need to embrace IoT.

A Deloitte Insights article[7] defines IoT as "a suite of technologies and applications that equip devices and locations to generate information and connect those devices and locations for instant data analysis and ideally, "smart" action." The IoT information value cycle elements include business activities, sensors producing data, and data analysis at the edge or cloud. The data analysis should lead to insights and use of the information to implement optimized decisions.

Further expansion of the value cycle elements includes manufacturing goods, marketing and selling, managing suppliers, managing people, finance and risk, and research and development. Sensors track humidity, temperature, acceleration, ambient light, acoustics, vibration, movement, and location. The data collected are big, descriptive, predictive, and cognitive analytics. The analysis insight helps predict production delays, the need to increase maintenance capacity, potential missed shipping deadlines, and customers' arrival. In addition, the insights support decisions that automatically order more parts, notify a technician to complete a physical inspection and alert guests that the desired product is available via mobile device wayfinding.

McKinsey & Company[8] recommends a narrower focus of IoT to Industrial IoT (IIoT) to collect manufacturing data that needs to be analyzed, allowing managers to glean insight and take appropriate actions. They suggest for effective IIoT, businesses need to overcome six myths. The first is that IIoT is only a dashboard. The benefit of IIoT is a shift in thinking around value creation where companies can use real-time data to accelerate problem resolution. The second is that IIoT will displace workers. The reality is that it will eliminate the need for employees to do dangerous or repetitive work and shift them to reskilled positions to accelerate the further implementation of new technologies. A third myth is that it is only a viable option for greenfield sites. Innovative manufacturers will adapt and optimize digital technologies for original equipment added to the plant with sensors, apps, and connectivity to existing equipment. A fourth myth is that 100% readiness is a prerequisite for digital adoption. Those that had already adopted partial IIoT were better able to respond more readily as they navigated the COVID-19 pandemic, showing that it is better to be moving forward with implementation than to continue planning.

Believing that it is costly to improve IIoT performance continuously is the fifth myth. The early adopters of digital technology find that efficiencies and productivity quickly offset implementation costs. The final debunked myth is that IIoT is not feasible for emerging economies. The results have shown that emerging economy facilities had 20% of digital technology adoption due to fewer legacy systems burdens. With a better understanding of the capabilities, we will now look at the most common industrial uses of IIoT.

A TATA survey[9] on IIoT adoption found the three most widely adopted implementations. Leading the way is real-time asset monitoring. Companies connect machinery and systems to monitor real-time compliance, reliability, and safety in local and remote locations. The result is making timely decisions to increase overall productivity, inventory maximization, prevention of quality issues, and augmented logistics. The second most adopted digital technology connects operational intelligence. Manufacturers can connect equipment in an intelligent network to quickly identify and resolve production issues. The final technology is the predictive maintenance of assets. The ability to track production processes and detect problems before creating costly downtime is an opportunity to reduce manufacturing costs significantly. While many digital technologies are available, these three are the most widely used to date.

Manufacturers who fail to adopt digital technology will be left behind. Forward-thinking plant operations will integrate IIoT in both greenfield and brownfield facilities. The highly integrated future factory has real-time monitoring that allows for data analysis, leading to solution selection and effective implementation of optimal solutions. Ultimately, technology leads to excellent safety, higher productivity, increased machine uptime, quality monitoring, inventory control, and enhanced shipments.

THE ADVANCE OF THE ROBOTS

The International Federation of Robotics reported[10] 2015 results that robot density in the Americas was 84 per 10,000 employees. The United States ranks among the top ten most automated countries globally. As this method's performance improves, the numbers will continue to rise to resolve manufacturing companies' issues, like the growing hiring gap.

In *Robot-ready: Adopting a new generation of industrial robots*,[11] Pricewaterhouse Coopers (PwC) shares a list of manufacturing operations strategies that choose to expand or introduce robotics to the shop floor. The first is developing a business case without surprises, outlining actual costs and clear performance targets, evaluating lease vs. buy options, and creating a streamlined budget approval process. The second is to assess organizational capabilities to implement and maintain robotic applications. The final strategy is to understand the intended process functionality thoroughly. Adopting this technology requires significant upfront and ongoing investment in the right technologies for favorable payback.

The PwC article shares many forms of robotic applications. Fixed and caged robots are stationary for traditional assembly, die casting, drilling, painting, picking, packing, riveting, sorting, and welding operations. Collaborative robots can work with machine operators to automate repetitive, dangerous, and monotonous tasks to support in-plant transport, materials handling, point-of-sale assembly, product and asset inspection, and robotic 3D printing. Collaborative autonomous mobile robots provide automated palletizing, in-plant transportation, product and shelf warehouse scanning, and robot materials handling. Additional forms include crewless aerial vehicles of drones for payloads under 15 pounds, asset inspection, asset management, autonomous data mapping, containment detection, inventory tracking and control, low payloads, and surveillance. The final application to share is robotic exoskeletons worn by operators to augment physical performance through carrying, gripping, and lifting. Overall, a wide variety of robotics forms are helpful in many ways to support production operations.

A highly evolving state of robotics continues to advance toward previously unseen capabilities. An example is an *IndustryWeek* article[12] on developing technology mimicking a human hand's touch. Unfortunately, the forecast for the development of this function is at least five years from becoming commercially viable. However, the potential to use piezoelectric effect-based sensors stacked in piezoresistive flexible films to replicate human touch would greatly expand robotic applications across various industries.

Capgemini Consulting conducted a 2016 study[13] on robotic process automation that can transform back-office operations using robotic process automation. Businesses see this as a transformational digital application that will reduce employees' need to do repetitive tasks using advanced software to automate complex processes. The technology benefits tasks that occur 50-60 or more times a day; conversion of data format and graphics; ERP and other back office transactions; mass email generation, archiving, and extracting; periodic reporting, data entry, and data analysis; and process list and file storage. The potential applications can improve every operation in a manufacturing facility.

A viable intersection of current operations and integrating robotics will allow manufacturers to move their organizations toward the desired future. Simultaneously, the work is not for the faint of heart when implementing sophisticated technology. However, if done well, it will deliver solutions for declining interest in low-end production work, increased employee productivity, reductions in repetitive use injuries, and enhanced safety.

EMBEDDED TECHNOLOGY

According to McKinsey & Company's article, a standard approach to tracking manufacturing plants' performance often includes compliance failures, customer complaints, first-pass yield deviations, recalls, rejects, and rework.[14] These are lagging indicators that are often not uniformly applied across locations. There is also a failure to accurately track the actual cost of quality issues. While there may be general knowledge of quality concerns across the plant, managers still may be averse to risk, leading to a failure to solve problems creatively and instead rely on increased quality checks and paperwork-based compliance. While this is acceptable when competitors use the same system, it becomes a disadvantage when others successfully adopt advanced technologies.

The advancement of technology will allow those in the manufacturing sector to approach or even achieve zero defects in the products reaching their customers. The measurement science will integrate the embedded metrology into the equipment, allowing 100% inspection and real-time response to quality defects. The state of embedded metrology will positively alter manufacturing.

Embedded systems[15] are computer hardware systems using microprocessors and software to perform dedicated functions. These can be stand-alone or integrated with other operations to provide real-time metrology feedback. Embedded system elements include a sensor that measures the physical detail, an analog-to-digital converter that converts the analog sensor signal to a digital signal, and a processor that evaluates the data and stores it in memory. A digital-to-analog converter changes it back to a signal where an actuator assesses the result and responds appropriately.

A Metrology News article[16] predicts that more intelligent factories will speed up operations while enhancing manufacturing dependability. Instead of batch operations with random sampling, embedded metrology will provide quality conformance of every part and reduce or eliminate the waste associated with scrap produced using past inspection practices. In addition, embedding the technology into each operation removes the need to pull a product from the line for inspection and integrates the process, allowing all functions to work cooperatively and connected. The result is a real-time response that maintains product quality conformance.

G²Métric[17] is involved in the design of measurement systems for aerospace manufacturer Airbus. They had adapted embedded metrology to four previous versions of Airbus programs. The Airbus 350 program was the first in which embedded metrology was a part of the initial design and build of the production processes. The end goal was to build a standard approach to the metrology systems, software, and data management architecture used at all European Airbus facilities. The result is a process that follows parts through each operation step. Each subassembly is measured and passed to the next step in an as-built value, not nominal. A simulation of the assembly evolves as the process progresses to provide feedback to the actuators and tool-

ing, allowing for an opportunity to adjust to end assembly requirements for fit and function on the fly.

Jiang, Tong, and Li wrote a chapter[18] titled *On-Machine Measurement System and Its Application in Ultra-Precision Manufacturing*, offering
a comprehensive review of embedded measurement systems. These
include contact profilometer systems, machine vision, confocal chro-
matic microscopy, optical interferometry, phase-shifting interferometry,
vertical scanning interferometry, wavelength scanning interferometry,
dispersive interferometry, and phase-measuring deflectometry. While
contact methods have been the norm due to technology maturity, they
operate at slow speeds and are unsuitable for some materials. The
authors found that the best approach is robust interferometry for ultra-
precision machining applications.

Ultimately manufacturing operations can continue with the status
quo with traditional quality methods or consider embracing embedded
metrology. Why should you decide on the latter option? The technology will result in cost savings, time savings, and throughput
improvements. Those who choose to adopt embedded technology will
ultimately become more competitive. They will also reduce the current
negative impact on the scrap environment that results from the lagging
indicators approach, another instance in which one can do well by
doing good.

CLOSING COMMENTS

As seen in the content shared in this chapter, the advancement of
process technologies will significantly alter the manufacturing industry. As a result, plant operations must evolve their processes to maintain or surpass their global competitors to ensure long-term survival.
As a result, notable innovations in processing opportunities will lead
to significant disruption in the manufacturing sector.

CHAPTER REFLECTION QUESTIONS

Do you consider the following when developing new manufacturing
processes?

- Adaptability and flexibility?
- Energy consumption?
- Environmental impact?
- Operational safety?
- Personal health?
- Total lifetime manufacturing cost?
- Waste management?

Are you integrating Industry 4.0 into your processes?

How does the adoption of humanist commitments align with your thoughts on the content of this chapter?

RECOMMENDED READING

AMPOWER Report 2022 on Additive Manufacturing

Debugging Embedded and Real-Time Systems: The Art, Science, Technology, and Tools of Real-Time System Debugging (2020) – Arnold S. Berger - Amazon.com Services LLC

Industrial Internet of Things: Technologies and Research Directions (2022) - Anand Sharma, Sunil Kumar Jangir, et al. – CRC Press

Industrial robots and cobots: Everything you need to know about your future co-worker (2019) – Michal Gurgul – Self-Published

The Fourth Industrial Revolution (2017) – Klaus Schwab – Random House Audio

CHAPTER 9
SUSTAINABLE OPERATIONS

"We don't have to engage in grand, heroic actions to participate in change. Small acts, when multiplied by millions of people, can transform the world."

—HOWARD ZINN

The manufacturing industry consumes many resources to produce products and services for its customers. Unfortunately, the current impact of many plant operations creates environmental, financial, and social harm to the company and its many internal and external stakeholders. Thankfully there are initial means to move toward net-zero impact, while some are taking it to the next level of becoming regenerative operations. We will explore the work of exemplars leading the path towards making these goals a feasible reality for all manufacturers. While far from an inclusive list of those with sustainable operations, the chapter content provides several examples of initiatives that can lead to cleaner manufacturing.

THE HARBEC JOURNEY

Bob Bechtold's journey[1] to sustainable manufacturing began with a customer requirement in 1996 when his company HARBEC was required to become *ISO 9001 Quality management systems*[2] certified. Bechtold, the company founder, and the president shared that they hated the requirement because they had to "do what we say and say what we do." The next step was integrating *ISO 14001 Environmental management systems – Requirements with guidance for use*[3] in 2002 when they installed their first wind turbine.

The company further benefited by adopting the *ISO 50001 Energy management systems – Requirements with guidance*[4] to lessen their energy costs. The machining, tooling, and injection molding company in Ontario, NY, continued conversion with a mindset that led to achieving a goal in 2013 of a zero carbon footprint.

HARBEC has adopted many available technologies[5] to be a sustainable manufacturing operation through a purpose-driven attack on all forms of waste. In addition, the company has implemented a wide-ranging set of sustainability initiatives that include:

Equipment

- Energy-efficient equipment – A transition from hydraulic to all-electric molding machines reduced energy usage by 50%.
- 100% green fleet – The company uses hybrids, all-electric, and bio-diesel vehicles.

Energy

- On-site renewable energy source – The company installed an initial wind turbine in 2002 and the second one in 2010, meeting approximately 60% of their needs for electrical power.
- Utility connection to green power – The company is a US EPA Green Power Partner and purchases the balance of its energy needs through renewable electricity.

- Efficient lighting – A recent second lighting upgrade from high efficiency to LED bulbs reduced energy consumption by 45%.
- Carbon offsetting – The purchase of carbon offsets counterbalances the balance of their CO_2 emissions that the company does not eliminate.
- Co-generation – Microturbine generators use compressed natural gas to produce electricity. The hot exhaust is used in a heat exchanger to transfer the heat to the water in a radiant floor heating system in the colder months and sent to absorptive chillers in the summer to create chilled water for air conditioning.

Recycling

- Water conservation and re-use – An 800K gallon reservoir captures and holds rainwater as a thermal mass to dissipate heat from process wastewater before sending it to a cooling tower, reducing overall cooling requirements.
- Ecostones™ - Producing these stones uses scrap plastic as an alternative to dolomite. These plastic stones have twice the surface area and voids to remediate parking lot runoff.
- Reusing waste – The company assembles reusable packing products to minimize landfill waste and reuses corrugated materials until the cardboard is exhausted.

Sustainable building design

- LEED™[6] warehouse – A "green" warehouse following the Leadership in Energy and Environmental Design guidelines, including daylight gathering, double insulated walls and roof, and in-floor radiant heating.

The extensive list shows no one way to become a manufacturer with a zero carbon footprint. The success of the many initiatives still falls short of zero emissions, which requires HARBEC to purchase carbon offsets to reach this level. HARBEC continues to explore and adopt alternative methods to reduce its carbon footprint.

HARBEC is a smaller company requiring them to be ingenious and innovative. As a result, recognition led to awards such as:

- Environmental Protection Agency Energy Star Small Business Award – The award was given in 2002 to recognize their leadership in using energy-efficient practices.
- Manufacturing Extension Partnership Excellence in Sustainability Award – The National Institute of Standards and Technology presented this award to HARBEC in 2011 for their outstanding work in developing and adopting green/sustainable practices.

Some manufacturers have chosen a race to the bottom to produce less expensive and higher-quality products. Others like HARBEC are shifting to a focus on environmental and societal needs through the reinvention of manufacturing. Their work has led to them becoming and maintaining carbon-neutral manufacturing status since 2013.

K'NEXING A SUSTAINABLE FACTORY

Michael Araten[7] is the President and CEO of Sterling Drive Ventures, LP. Sterling is the family office with multiple businesses, including The Rodon Group (Rodon). Araten joined in 2005 as their Vice President and General Counsel. He became President and COO in 2006 and was named President and CEO in 2009. Rodon is a highly automated plastics injection molder doing small plastic parts for various businesses. A particular fun focus is their production of the K'NEX[8] components, an educational toy developed by Joel Glickman, his father-in-law. Rodon is an example of a company that has profoundly ingrained sustainability into its manufacturing operations

Rodon has embedded an ethos of environmental sustainability. As a result, the company has become one of the leaders in responsible manufacturing in the plastic injection molding industry. Examples of their initiatives include:

- Landfill-free solutions – The company was among the first in its industry to receive the Sustainable Waste Solutions (SWS) recognition as a Landfill Free Facility.
- SWS logo – All Rodon manufacturing waste ships to SWS to be recycled or processed into advanced energy-from-waste facilities.
- Packaging conservation – The large volume resins of nearly ten million pounds annually are bought in bulk and stored in silos. They currently recycle twenty percent of the incoming cardboard, increasing the percentage yearly. Outgoing cardboard reductions come from cartons shipped from Rodon that hold 300-400% more product than the original packaging. The company also offers customers a returnable and reusable packaging program.
- Energy conservation – Rodon is a member of Direct Energy Business with programs that allow them to improve energy usage. These programs range from basic improvements like motion-sensor activation lighting to more sophisticated demand responses to reducing energy consumption during peak periods.
- PPL logo – The PPL Electric Utilities Corporation has recognized the company for its energy-efficient initiatives and added them to the E-Power Energy-Smart Business Honor Roll.
- Nontoxic materials – All materials used in manufacturing are guaranteed to be nontoxic and nonhazardous. The resins used in the large-volume injection modeling processes are certified for this status by the FDA, RoHS, REACH, and NSF. As a result, they improve the environment and the safety of their employees, customers, and end-users of the products they produce.
- Environmental stewardship – The Rodon workforce fully supports the single-stream recycling program at the plant. The company also contracts with AERC Recycling Solutions to provide a way for employees and their family members to

recycle batteries, computer equipment, electronics, and used lights from their households.

The company has been a long-term champion of corporate responsibility and a committed steward of the environment.

When building the new Rodon plant in 1987, they incorporated new practices and technologies that resulted in a green factory.[9] In addition to the above items, robots allow the operation to run 24/7, but additional benefits include efficiency improvement and waste reduction. The excess plastic from each produced part is reground and recycled for reuse in the manufacturing process. The robots are programmed to do this at the optimal moment where the timing eliminates resin material waste. Robots stack the in-process materials precisely, which results in packaging cost savings. The technology reduces part distortion allowing triple or quadruple the number of components in each carton. The result is a reduction in cardboard usage and landfill waste leading to additional positive environmental impact.

Rodon's dedication to a healthy and vital environment includes a societal obligation to foster sustainability to minimize the impact on the local community. The company clearly understands that manufacturers produce too much trash and consume too much electricity. Therefore, the company drove initiatives resulting in a 20-50% reduction in electric usage. Manufacturing engineers work to optimize each product produced through the injection molding machine, where a hybrid of hydraulic and electric power is generally the best option. Further process enhancement utilizes Eco-Indicator 99[10] (EI'99) methodology, a life-cycle assessment weighing method to produce quantifiable measures of "environmental friendliness."

TAKING THE TRANE TO SUSTAINABLE OPERATIONS

Dave Regnery is the new CEO and member of the Board of Directors[11] of Trane Technologies as of June 2021. He was known as the president and chief operating officer who had worked in concert with the departing CEO of Mike Lamach. Lamach described Dave as the "co-architect of our transformation as a focused climate innovator." As a result, Trane would move forward with a leader that knows the industry, how to successfully integrate sustainability megatrends, an understanding of the needs of their customers, and how to maximize outcomes for company stakeholders. A career company man, he fully embraces the work to continue the position of Trane as a sustainable manufacturing exemplar.

Trane is committed to taking a leadership role in responsible manufacturing.[12] The company has plans that include:

- The gigaton challenge - The company has stated a goal of a one gigaton reduction of their customer's footprint by 2030. In addition, they are creating innovative technologies to increase the energy efficiency of the HVAC systems they manufacture, decrease food loss through refrigeration systems, and integrate next-generation refrigerants.
- Leading by example – Trane works through a restorative environment approach throughout the company and its supply chain. The focus is on becoming a carbon-neutral operation with zero landfill waste, net positive water use, and a ten percent reduction in energy consumption.
- Creating opportunity for all – An inclusive approach is underway to become a workforce that reflects their community, provides gender parity in leadership positions, and provides green STEM career pathways.
- Environmental actions – Trane seeks to be part of the solution in reducing record greenhouse gas emissions, solving the issues arising from increased urbanization, and slowing the ever-growing energy and resource consumption demand.
- Social – Our people and citizenship – They are investing in creating more significant opportunities for their teams and communities. The work focuses on long-term well-being through improved economic mobility and quality of life.
- Governance and accountability – The board of directors and councils have strong sustainability governance structures to

evaluate the organization's climate risk and sustainability initiatives.

Trane's comprehensive plan produces the results that show they are achieving the desired objectives.

CLIMATE TAKE BACK™

Interface has taken its work as a manufacturing sustainability exemplar to the next level with a 25-year plan to go further with a new mission of Climate Take Back™. The program intends to build on past success and share it with others. In their guide, the reader will learn about moonshot goals, how to change a mindset, and the role of vision in achieving the plan. Additional key concepts include: a circular approach to business, the need to engage everyone, the path is not linear, the importance of transparency, the ripple can become a wave, and the need to raise the bar continually. Finally, based on the past 25 years of success, Interface is a model for others to follow as they shift from sustainability to a regenerative approach to business.

Interface is developing a factory[13] that will positively contribute to the forest using biomimicry design. In addition, the manufacturing facility will provide ecosystem service to the area landscape. Biomimicry 3.8 was a supporter in the redesign of its Lagrange, GA factory providing three critical guiding principles:

1. Resetting the company mindset toward a revised North Star of higher ambition.
2. Setting performance goals using the surrounding ecosystem as a baseline.
3. Using site-specific details to develop the design concepts for the manufacturing facility.

Elements of the ecosystem given consideration were biodiversity support, carbon sequestration, sediment retention, soil fertility, and water storage and purification.

PRINCIPLES OF A REGENERATIVE ECONOMY

A key aspect of transformational vision as a humanist manufacturer is to become a regenerative business. The Capital Institute led the development of the *8 Principles of a Regenerative Economy*.[14] The fundamental interconnected principles include:

1. In right relationship – There is no absolute separation between us and the ecosphere.
2. Views wealth holistically – Capital goes beyond money in the bank, where harmony includes cultural, experiential, living, and social wealth.
3. Innovative, adaptive, responsive – Adaptability and innovation are essential to our health as we respond to the ever-present and accelerating rates of global change.
4. Empowered participation – Our interdependent system requires the whole system's fitness, active, and responsible engagement.
5. Honors community and place – The beliefs, institutions, peoples, and traditions are unique to communities respecting personal history and place.
6. Edge effect abundance – The system edges are home to the weakest bonds in the dominant pattern, allowing opportunities for cross-fertilization and innovation.
7. Robust circulatory flow – An economic system needs a similar pattern to total human health, where human networks efficiently reuse materials supported by the open circulation of information and money.
8. Seeks balance – Regenerative economic health requires a balance of competition and collaboration, efficiency and resilience, coherence and diversity, and the needs of small, medium, and large enterprises.

Becoming an eventual regenerative organization requires thinking and acting in new and different ways. The company leadership must choose how to explore personal and organizational change far beyond the current knowledge base. For too long, a common approach to business has been exploiting and extracting a community's resources that an organization values. When the company depletes the natural resources in a locale, they leave that one to find that next that supports their needs while leaving a hollow shell of a community behind. As our world shrinks and expands in population, this practice cannot continue.

CLOSING REMARKS

The development of sustainable facilities moving toward net-zero impact or further toward regeneration will have a significant effect. All internal stakeholders benefit from working or living where multiple plant operations can collectively improve the global environment. A positive benefit[15] of the COVID-19 pandemic was that as the world shut down and isolated, the environment saw significant improvement in a short time frame. There was a quick improvement of air quality in large cities, less water pollution, as seen in one example of the canals in Venice, Italy, and a beneficial reduction in greenhouse gas emissions.

CHAPTER REFLECTION QUESTIONS

Which of your production facilities' resources is causing the most collective environmental, financial, and social harm?

Which of your production facilities' resources are low-hanging fruit that requires little or no investment to implement?

What programs are available in your area to support investment in resource use reduction?

Is becoming a sustainable or regenerative manufacturing operation based on humanist commitments vital to you?

Before you are ready to lead your company through transformative change, is there personal growth you need to embrace?

RECOMMENDED READING

Let's Start the Climate Take Back (2022) – Interface – https://www.interface.com/EU/en-GB/sustainability/climate-take-back-en_GB

The Future of Energy: The 2021 guide to the energy transition - renewable energy, energy technology, sustainability, hydrogen, and more (2021) – John Armstrong – Energy Technology Publishing

The Regenerative Business: Redesign Work, Cultivate Human Potential, Achieve Extraordinary Outcomes (2017) – Carol Sanford – Nicholas Brealey Publishing

PHASE 4

EMPLOYEE CENTRIC

4. Creation of an employee-centric workforce where each member, team, and organization has an opportunity to move toward full human potential.

An employee-centric focus is essential to becoming a humanist manufacturing operation. The previous phases share examples of considerations necessary to set up a desirable plant operation for younger generations to consider as a career option. They expect that their values will align with the values of their employers. The humanist commitments match their desire to be contributing members of society.

Chapter 10 begins with the value of creating optimal tension for each employee. We all have a point on the curve between the extremes of no pressure to perform and too much pressure. Finding that sweet spot between the two extremes allows for the potential of a maximum contribution from each employee. There is also an emphasis on the need to improve employee engagement, boost employee morale, rewire the human brain, recognition, reward, and other considerations around pay and benefits to support the needs of employees.

CHAPTER 10
PUTTING EMPLOYEES FIRST

"Silent gratitude isn't much to anyone."

—GERTRUDE STEIN

Business leaders like Richard Branson[1] recognize the value of attracting and retaining outstanding employees. A recent search for CEO concerns shared this common theme. Likewise, sound executives understand the need to build and maintain an influential company culture that appeals to promising business talent. It is one thing to know that this is important, but how is it accomplished?

My experience has been that many leaders fail to understand the value of creating high levels of employee morale. They get so consumed by the many challenges they face that they lose track of the state of employee satisfaction. I suspect I have a heightened awareness as I tend to be a person who battles my propensity to be all in or out when it comes to a sense of satisfaction with my superiors. However, what burns in me is when a leader's lack of proper attention harms my coworkers, particularly those I support in my responsibility area.

OPTIMAL TENSION

We will first explore the concept of "optimal tension" as a mechanical principle. Many machines use a belt and pulley system to turn various shafts. For example, individuals with an internal combustion engine who have opened their vehicle's hood will see a serpentine belt. The camshaft pulley often drives a belt that turns the air conditioning compressor, alternator, power steering pump, and water pump pullies. The proper operation relies on tensioning the belt at a level tight enough not to slip but not so tight that it puts too much side load on any of the shafts. The belt has a tight side where the drive shaft pulls the belt and minimal slack on the opposite side.

The belt example applies to motivating a workforce. The drive pulley is the leadership of an organization. The motor's RPMs turning the drive pulley are equivalent to setting the organization's pace, and the torque level is the change intensity. Like the automotive components in the above example, the pulleys are generally different diameters that we should consider when creating an ideal performance for each department. Furthermore, the belt's tight side can equate to the need to pull some people along, while the slack side would be those that will follow the lead. To create the highest potential for maximum motivation, the organization needs to design a plan that fits the varied needs of each workforce member. Each of us has a point where we can perform at an optimal level where our individuality and teamwork are not allowed to slip. Yet there is enough "optimal tension" to stretch us beyond our current performance expectations without causing damage.

I have heard others state that leaders need to treat everyone equally. I argue the better approach is to treat everyone differently but with fairness. Each employee finds motivation from something different than other members of the organization. For example, one past employee worked our second shift to pursue her dream of becoming a registered nurse. For this reason, I assigned her to a manufacturing line that did not typically have overtime requirements. Other employees would want all available overtime, so I would allocate them to the lines that worked the most hours and cross-trained them to work on other high-hour lines. For those who wanted to move up the company ladder, I would provide them with assignments that would help them develop the required skill set to be promoted and showcase their capabilities to those looking to fill positions. As leaders, we must know each person's motivation if we want to realize a highly dedicated workforce performing at their levels of optimal tension.

Developing a practical approach to building a highly engaged workforce is an opportunity to drive a significant increase in organizational profitability. However, while an increased profit margin is desirable, I would argue that we have a more important moral obligation to maximize the potential of our workforce. The good news is that creating motivated employees leads to more robust financial performance.

MUCH WORK TO BE DONE

The Gallup *State of the American Workforce*[2] report supports a significant need for increasing employee morale. Unfortunately, American workforce engagement is at 33%, startlingly low compared to the 70% result for the world's best companies. In the US, 16% of employees experience active disengagement. With only 33% engaged, that leaves 51% of the workforce in a state of just being present. We are significantly disadvantaged when two-thirds of the American workforce is not engaged in their work. The results are worse in manufacturing, with only 25% of employees experiencing workplace engagement. Given these poor results, we should look for successful examples for those who question whether factory workers can be highly committed to their job.

The *2020 Fortune 100 Best Places to Work For*[3] had five companies in the manufacturing and production category. A more in-depth investigation into the data looked at the Top Ten in the large and small/medium categories for this industry sector. The average score for "Employees say this is a great place to work" was 87% in the large class and 93% for the small/medium group. More telling was the word cloud results: the large companies' employees had "people" listed for five and "associates" for two of the top ten companies. The count for small/medium firms was six for "people" and one for "team" from the Top Ten list. Based on the importance of people making somewhere a great place to work, we should look at who can significantly improve employee morale.

BOOSTING EMPLOYEE MORALE

The research results in a McKinsey Quarterly article[4] place the responsibility for improving employee morale on the boss. Overall life satisfaction includes 25% of job satisfaction, and the impact of job satisfaction (39%) is integral to interpersonal relationships. The primary driver of satisfaction in interpersonal relationships was relationships with management at 86%. Therefore, if we accept that leadership is crucial in generating enhanced job satisfaction to increase morale, we should explore actions to achieve this desired result.

ACRA[5] supports the importance of employee morale as necessary, where the failure to do so will harm the bottom line. They provide a set of cost-effective and straightforward suggestions to enhance the opportunity to improve workforce engagement, including:

- A focus on the bigger picture – Employees need to understand the larger vision and their role in carrying out the organization's greater good.
- Creative celebrations of accomplishments – Showing appreciation and the value of workers to the company through innovative events.
- Pursuing passions – Find ways to allow personal passion projects to improve productivity.
- Routine disruption – Adding occasional activities that break up the routine include bringing in an ice cream truck or an appreciation lunch.
- Training in positive thinking – A skill that can be taught and will significantly increase overall morale.

These are just a few suggestions for low-cost yet high-impact strategies to improve employee morale.

A Forbes article[6] asks why some employees are highly engaged and motivated. The author found this occurs when they believe in their organization and "feel loved and inspired." Leaders successfully motivated the workforces at Atlassian, Google, and Microsoft. In addition, their leadership groups consistently inspire and motivate their employees. The author shares the following six strategies from these companies for enhancing motivation, which include:

- Establishing meaningful goals.
- Celebrating milestones from small through significant.
- Sharing valued feedback.
- Empowering employees.
- Leadership keeping promises.
- Continuing to evolve by learning what motivates the employees.

Adequately implemented technology to support these strategies enhances success in implementing these effectively and efficiently.

As shared earlier, my last plant manager position began at a manufacturing facility where several assembly lines had never made their daily production goals. I adopted several of the above approaches that led to improved job satisfaction. The one change I believe had the most significant impact was to go around at the end of the shift and write a positive note on the whiteboard that listed pertinent data for the line. Within six months, people routinely ran into my office with beaming smiles, exclaiming that they had made their production targets that day. A customer representative visited during this time frame and stated that he had never seen people work as hard as they did in our plant. I believe they felt "loved and inspired."

REWIRING THE HUMAN BRAIN

Our ability to understand the human brain continues to evolve as further research and technological capabilities allow additional insight into this complex organ. For example, we have recently begun to understand the role of mirror neurons. We can fire these to influence positive actions when we act and see it performed in others, thus enabling higher concepts like connection and compassion that employees can learn through mimicry. Therefore, leaders must understand how to recognize, understand, and manage our feelings to effectively and efficiently identify, understand, and influence the emotions of those in our care responsibly.

A WorkplaceInsight article[7] explains neuroplasticity as an ability to rewire the brain. Changes in the neural pathways occur through our experiences, which cause the brain to reorganize by repeating new favorable practices. Using neuroscience to reshape our behavior requires effort to change and adapt the brain to feel motivated and apply the necessary focus. Through repetition and practice, the new neural pathways strengthen. Cognitive-behavioral therapy (CBT), meditation, and mindfulness enhance neuroplasticity through repeated training and stillness. Ultimately, just as physical fitness requires regular and balanced exercise to reshape the body, those wanting to rewire the brain must do good work to achieve the desired result. We will next explore why rewiring the brain is crucial for us.

A blog post[8] by Judy Hersch introduces the Hebbian Law of Repetition, Donald Hebb's discovery of the "fire together, wire together" model of nerve cells' function. The shared example was learning to drive, which I related to my experience of taking hot air balloon flight lessons. Initially, I had to work extremely hard to pay attention to how much and when to add heat, watch out for other aircraft, pay attention to the flight path, and communicate with the chase crew. Additional focus required monitoring fuel usage, keeping an eye on the weather, knowing the wind directions and speeds at various altitudes, and planning to land the balloon safely at the end of the flight, allowing easy retrieval. Rewiring my brain allowed me to work fluidly through the requirements needed for this new skill. As we work to motivate our workforce to maximize their potential, we must understand that they will be working through this rewiring of their brain that will require time to become adept at new actions.

EMPLOYEE RECOGNITION AND REWARD

We all have a built-in desire to receive appreciation and recognition. When employees adopt new desirable behaviors, businesses should distribute appropriate rewards. For example, a *2022 Global Culture Report*[9] saw an 18x increase in employees' probability of great work when receiving authentic gratitude and acknowledgment of their contributions to the organization. They were 11x more likely to stay another year and 3x more likely to be with the organization in three years. Best-in-class recommendations[10] are:

- Make recognition an experience – Recognize employees in a respectful and fun manner.
- Create a flexible program that grows with your company – Different employees are motivated in different ways, so it is essential to provide options that meet the individual's interests.
- Base your recognition program around your company values – Companies that align recognition around their values will deepen the level of employee commitment to achieving them.
- Build a connection with recognition – Programs can build a sense of community by acknowledging employees that go above expectations to help customers or colleagues, celebrate milestones, or reward a positive attitude, particularly with remote teams or during disruption.
- Center your culture around recognition – A people-oriented culture puts its employees first and continues to show appreciation for employee contributions to organizational success.
- Make every recognition reward personal – Provide rewards that keep the company location in mind and reflect individual preferences.
- Celebrate every work anniversary – If anniversary celebrations exist for any employee group, all workgroups should receive similar recognition.

- Offer timely, immediate recognition – Appreciation of recognition diminishes over time.
- Build a multidirectional appreciation system -- Move from a top-down approach to one that allows colleagues to express appreciation in any direction within the company.
- Integrate recognition – A company should embed the awarding of recognition and appreciation into its culture.

A humanist manufacturing environment will be one where recognition and appreciation of others will likely occur. Therefore, ensuring that employees receive proper acknowledgment for their role in its success is vital.

If employees successfully achieve the goals of an organization, it is essential to reward them fairly and equitably. There is a wide range of options available with the following from a Society of Human Resource Management article:[11]

- Annual incentive plan – Rewards are tied to the achievement of yearly goals.
- Discretionary bonus plan – The company reviews the results of a periodic review to determine if they desire to award a bonus and how much and to whom they should distribute them.
- Spot awards – A reward to recognize a contribution to a short-term project or task.
- Profit-sharing plan - A distribution of a portion of company profits earned during a defined time frame, typically through a prescribed formula and distribution.
- Gain-sharing plans – Incentive programs with a focus on sharing productivity gains.
- Team/small-group sharing – Plans that look at distributing bonuses for the excellent performance of a whole group.
- Retention bonus - Money in addition to an employee's salary to keep them with the company, particularly if the organization would struggle if a key employee left.

- Project bonus – Additional compensation for bringing an assignment to fruition in an accelerated manner.

The level of importance will vary from one employee to another. It is also a poor antidote to keep someone otherwise willing to leave the company. However, appropriately sharing financial gains has the potential to improve human thriving.

ADDITIONAL CONSIDERATIONS

Employers willing to commit to the humanist manufacturing framework must establish a work environment that rewards employees for their work to support carrying out the "why," the vision, mission, and values. Responsible leaders will work to build on or integrate the following:

- Diversity, equity, and inclusion – A workplace that exhibits and embraces differences in age, ethnicity, gender, gender identity, race, sexual orientation, and socioeconomic class, one where programs and processes are fair and impartial and allow each equal individual access to possible outcomes. Finally, support individuals to be authentic in a welcoming and comfortable environment that promotes a sense of belonging.
- Emergency financial support – Development of a program that can assist employees with financial products or services to meet emergency needs through payroll advance or low-interest loans.
- Employee well-being – Establish and design wellness programs to achieve higher productivity, improve morale and loyalty, reduce injuries, eliminate disability-related costs, and lessen absenteeism.
- Employee stock ownership plan – Plans that allow employees to become partial owners of their company lead to an alternative exit strategy for aging owners, attracting

top talent with higher retention, increased productivity, no change in governance, and tax advantages.

- Healthcare – Appropriate health insurance can attract good employees, boost employee satisfaction, reduce absenteeism, and save your employees money.
- Living wage – Paying the workforce a living wage is an investment in a healthy community and a robust local economy. The employer benefits from decreased costs, favorable community image, improved employee productivity, and increased employee loyalty. Employees benefit from experiencing less financial stress and a better quality of life for themselves and their families.
- Professional development – Subsidize training and education that supports the company's "why," vision, mission, and values.
- Retirement plan – Employers benefit by attracting and retaining quality employees and tax deductions. In addition, employees are rewarded appropriately for their contribution to the company's success, proportional to their years of service.

A recurring theme is that proper benefits are an investment in the essential elements of the business – its employees. The return on the associated costs is higher productivity and employee satisfaction. Ultimately it is also the right thing for those organizations committed to the humanist manufacturing framework.

CLOSING COMMENTS

We must do something different to attract the next generation of manufacturing employees. For example, an article in Industry Week[12] shares a need to begin inspiring the next generation in K-12, provide the latest technology, embrace their ideas, recognize their performance, and create a desirable culture of trust and managerial accountability. In addition, it would be necessary to investigate further what motivators and benefits drive potential local employees to join our organizations.

If we invest properly in developing a highly motivated workforce, we have the most significant potential as a thriving organization that attracts and retains high-caliber employees.

CHAPTER REFLECTION QUESTIONS

Do you have an employee engagement strategy that includes the following?

- Effective and efficient ongoing tracking of employee engagement?
- An ability to quickly respond when issues arise?
- Is employee engagement an ongoing priority at all levels of the company?
- Are managers empowered to drive employee engagement?

Is there an employee well-being strategy that has the following elements?

- Belonging and contributing?
- Physical health and lasting behavior change?
- Security and safety?
- Social connections?
- Stress reduction and resilience?
- Wonder and creativity?

RECOMMENDED READING

Pay Matters: The Art and Science of Employee Compensation (2020) – David Weaver – Lioncrest Publishing

The Culture Blueprint: A Guide to Building the High-Performance Workplace (2015) – Robert Richman – Creative Commons Attribution–Share Alike 4.0 International License

PHASE 5

 **POSITIVE
EXTERNAL IMPACT**

5. Ongoing positive impact on
critical external stakeholders
to create an ecosystem of
community thriving.

Humanist manufacturing operations can potentially be a vital contributor in work to develop thriving communities. Therefore, in Chapter 11, there is a significant focus on considering previously underutilized employee pools. The reasons for overlooking them are often due to a lack of understanding of employment personnel's unique but reasonable needs for work accommodations.

Many in these alternative pools need help transitioning to a thriving place of employment that leads to a sense of belonging. The chapter looks at a few workforce integration models to help them eliminate their constraints to full potential jobs.

There is also a need to revitalize communities that are experiencing deindustrialization. The High-Roads Industrial Commons model is one approach to bringing back these negatively impacted communities that previous manufacturers have abandoned.

CHAPTER 11
BUILDING THRIVING COMMUNITIES

"There is no power for change greater than a community discovering what it cares about."

—Margaret J. Wheatley

Most of us have seen what we know as Russian nesting dolls.[1] They are dolls made from wood where subsequent smaller versions fit inside the next larger one. Likewise, communities are a nested system to include 1) the home, 2) a district or neighborhood, 3) the city, and 4) a region.

Manufacturing operations that desire to impact their community positively should begin by asking what keeps those in each household from thriving at home. Next, the group would repeat the process at the neighborhood level, then the city, and finally the region. As we lift one another, we collectively lift the entire community.

Ultimately, I encourage the manufacturing industry to reach a point that allows each citizen of the world an opportunity to meet at a minimum their needs for just and healthy lives, with a full opportunity to achieve their highest potential. This chapter will explore additional options to improve thriving in the community to reach this Big Hairy Audacious Goal.

We have addressed several elements that contribute to thriving communities in earlier chapters. For example, adopting the ten humanist commitments includes many vital features, including altruism, empathy, environmentalism, humility, social justice, and service. Additionally, Chapter Six consists of a B Impact Assessment adoption recommendation that includes community, customers, environment, governance, and workers categories that support many aspects of being a responsible member of the community in which an organization operates. We have also done an exploration of sustainable product design and material selection. Next, setting up sustainable operations contributes to a better local environment. Finally, providing a living wage and appropriate benefits allows employees to contribute substantially to their local economy. We will look at a significant employment challenge for manufacturing operations with alternative hiring pools to close the gap and an approach to revitalizing deindustrialized communities that are additional opportunities to create a thriving community.

ALTERNATIVE HIRING POOLS

The research results[2] in a 2018 partnership of Deloitte and The Manufacturing Institute found double-digit growth rates in manufacturing job openings since mid-2017. At a historic high of 89%, the number one issue for manufacturing executives is filling the gap between available employment candidates and their plant operations' needs. The case will become even more pressing, with 2.6 million baby boomers expected to retire in the coming decade.

The manufacturing sector participant looking for a noble purpose can help typically overlooked groups build more secure employment futures. A business interested in developing opportunities for those historically disenfranchised will first need to create a trusting climate. Then, the firm's representatives must work with the community wisdom leaders to build an employment pathway for the various populations.

My experience in manufacturing is that women primarily worked on the shop floor, mainly doing work that was the assembly of small components like electronics or jobs in the quality department. Since approximately half of the world population is women, that is an apparent first group to explore. Additionally, as the manufacturing industry evolves from dirty smoke-belching facilities to technology-infused clean operations, it will be essential to understand how to attract, retain, and promote women in all areas and levels in our factories.

The sourcing organization Thomas interviewed[3] six women in the industry, asking for must-read advice for those wanting to follow them. Denise Ebenhoech, regional head of advanced robotic applications for KUKA Robotics Corp, sees that things are improving where women are in higher areas of responsibility at a younger age than when she entered the workforce 25 years earlier. Lessening bias is critical for Ginger Butz, a business segment manager at The Morey Corporation. She further suggests that companies recruiting women should partner with organizations like Women in Manufacturing.[4] Lindsey Harding, accounting manager at Stone Interiors, recommends developing training programs to create opportunities for women to succeed in manufacturing. These are just a few of the many ideas shared by those thriving in this industry. Furthermore, an additional benefit is from research in a McKinsey & Company article, *Women in the Workplace 2020,*[5] where stock share performance and profits can be nearly 50 percent higher when women have prominent executive management representation.

If everyone is having difficulty finding qualified new employees, they would likely be interested in those who exhibit the following ideal workplace traits:[6]

- Attention to detail.
- Ability to work with little supervision.
- Comfortable with repetitive aspects of work.
- Desire to deliver high-quality service.
- Problem-solving skills.
- Successful within roles requiring physical exertion.

Individuals with these qualifications are surprisingly facing an unemployment rate of 85%. If you think there must be a catch, these potential workers are on the autism spectrum, otherwise known as a segment of neurodiversity.

Lexington[7] explored career opportunities for those with autism. The organization sees the traits of intense focus and a need for structure as particularly beneficial to those employed to do assembly-line work. An assembler repeats the same actions repeatedly over the entire work shift. When properly matched with individuals on the spectrum, the work resulted in a high-quality standard. A job seen as tedious to many can be a source of enjoyment and pride to employees with autism. If these traits can be a good match, we should encourage manufacturing companies to recognize this opportunity.

The next group is our returning veterans. Over the many years of my manufacturing career, I have often interviewed and hired many job candidates. My experience has been that if two candidates were otherwise equally qualified and one had served in the military, I would select the veteran. These individuals had a sense of duty and responsibility suited for the manufacturing industry.

Many veterans have known nothing other than military service, as they often enlist shortly after graduating high school. Twenty years later, they leave the familiarity of the work routine as an armed forces member. A transition to the civilian sector can be difficult for them. The manufacturing industry can be a natural fit given the attention to detail, a need to be precise, teamwork, troubleshooting, and spatial thinking required to succeed in this work environment. They can also replicate their military career's success and upward mobility in the manufacturing industry.

Another pool of potential employees is the formerly incarcerated or what some call returning citizens. Nehemiah Manufacturing Company and its Founder and CEO, Dan Meyer, give those with a criminal record another chance. Nehemiah is also trying to fix societal wrongs. For example, they are working to revitalize the inner city of Cincinnati, one of many that experienced significant economic damage when manufacturing operations left town in the pursuit of cheaper labor.

Other companies would be wise to look at Nehemiah's success in hiring those with criminal backgrounds. At 56 years of age, Franklin Comer worked at Nehemiah for nearly a year. He served 33 years in prison for aggravated robbery and murder. Comer knew he had made a significant mistake during his served time, took an inventory of himself, and decided to become a better person. Through the support of Cincinnati Works, he worked a job readiness program that led to employment with Nehemiah. Nehemiah is just one of many companies having success in hiring returning citizens.

In the mid-1990s, I worked as a project engineer for a stamping operation. The labor market during that period was like the one current employers are experiencing. One afternoon, I remember walking through the plant and seeing a man missing a leg. He was running a production operation while balancing himself on crutches. Reflecting on the experience, I am ashamed that my immediate thought was that we had hit the bottom of the barrel when hiring a man with one leg to work a manufacturing job.

My current self reflects on the earlier example of an employee where I first went to his leg that was missing. Instead, I should have considered what he brought to the job and what accommodation was necessary to increase his comfort and potential to succeed. I now see a need to shift from seeing disabilities to one focused on exploring capabilities. The Americans with Disabilities Act (ADA) became law in 1990. Yet, these many years later, I can count on one hand the number of people with visible disabilities who interacted with me during my working experience. It seems unlikely that none existed in the areas where I lived and worked, so more of them should have been seen at my employer's. It turns out that the companies were likely missing out on the benefits gained from hiring from this segment of our population.

The Lighthouse for the Blind, Inc.[8] provides meaningful manufacturing opportunities for the blind, DeafBlind (those with vision and hearing loss), and blind with other disabilities. In operation since 1918, they employ 480 employees, of which 270 have some form of blindness. Employment allows for various career opportunities and training programs.

Each of these employment pools is a viable option to work in manufacturing operations. Hiring them leads to capable workers that will likely stay with the company long-term as they seldom have other options. They will generally appreciate the opportunity for gainful employment and will be contributing members of the organization. Additionally, other employees will like working for a company willing to help those in these various segments of their local population.

INTEGRATING THESE NEW EMPLOYMENT CANDIDATE POOLS

Many of us are aware of the recruiter role used by the military to find those individuals they can entice to join the various military branches. They face a similar issue to the manufacturing industry of a declining percentage of individuals interested in beginning their adult life in military service. Their responsibility is to provide information regarding the training and career opportunities available in the five service branches.

An area industry recruiter could receive financial support from a collective of manufacturing plants, nonprofits, or government funding to target one or more of the area groups profiled in this chapter. The recruiter would work with the key players in the community. They could attend job and career fairs to meet potential employees. They could also develop relationships with the local high schools to provide further insight regarding the value of a manufacturing career for students.

The recruiter could also be the point person to gain community involvement in integrating these various groups into the manufacturing workforce. The first step is to determine the wisdom leaders in the community. In every locale, there are individuals that others look to as having the best interest at heart for their group. Identifying and assembling these wisdom leaders is the key to project success. In this case, we would build a community stakeholder alliance that would include those identified from the communities in which the students live, the school system, the manufacturing sector, workforce development, nonprofits, and funding agencies. The first questions to ask are who should be the alliance members. Then ask if they can work together. Membership evolves until everyone is willing to move forward as a guiding coalition. They must agree to only disagree behind closed doors and present a unified front externally.

WORKFORCE INTEGRATION MODEL PROGRAMS

An example of an alliance that is successfully working to support those facing various challenges and desiring to gain work with a living wage with career opportunities is Network2Work.[9] The program host is Piedmont Valley Community College (PVCC) in Charlottesville, Virginia. The Charlottesville Regional Chamber of Commerce (CRCC) found in 2011 that 29 percent of Charlottesville families could not meet their basic needs. For example, the costs of affordable daycare and reliable transportation were something they could not acquire due to existing financial constraints. Individuals wanted to do what was necessary to make conditions better for themselves and their families but needed initial help. As a result, CRCC and PVCC partnered to develop the Division of Community Self-Sufficiency Programs. One outcome of the work was developing the Network2Work tool that connects job seekers, employers, and support agencies with the ability to provide resources that allow them support during the difficult initial transition to meaningful employment. The January 2021 report found that 17 percent of families still are self-sufficiency challenged. However, the 12 percent improvement over ten years led to initial work at the state level to expand the program to other regions in the Commonwealth. Unfortunately, the expansion is on hold due to political leadership changes.

A second model program to consider is that of Greystone Bakery, a Certified B Corporation. Their "mission is their bakers." They have an Open Hiring Model[10] allowing those traditionally deemed unhireable, such as drug addicts and those with criminal records, an opportunity to complete an apprenticeship. Once hired, Greystone provides them access to community services and assistance to enhance the potential for employee success. In addition, a *Business Insider* article[11] looks at 16 other organizations benefiting society within this business community of Certified B Corporations.

These are just a few models of organizations that support companies wanting to integrate those from historically untargeted employment pools. Doing so is not without challenges but can be less complicated by partnering with organizations focusing on a particular segment of our population. For example, the Virginia Values Veterans[12] (V3) program is an organization helping to integrate veterans into manufacturing careers. In addition, rethink ED[13] supports companies that want to hire and retain the neurodiverse, including those on the autism spectrum. Other examples are seen earlier in the chapter, and others will follow in the balance of this content.

A THRIVING COMMUNITY EXEMPLAR

How does a company impact society and the environment with widely diverse business units of markets in agricultural/industrial containers, office furniture, polymer compounding, recycling/waste management, RFID asset management, and transportation? For Cascade Engineering, this includes acting on what they believe[14] in the following ways:

- Anti-racism – The company implemented diversity, equity, and inclusion long before it became a recent emphasis to become a politically correct standard practice.
- B Corp – The company is one of the largest B Corps[15] in the world.
- B Nice – A commitment to providing mental health assistance to employees and their families using the BE NICE[16] four-step action plan.
- Certifications – The additional certifications include International Automotive Taskforce, ISO 9000, ISO 14001, ISO/IEC 17025, Partners for a Racism Free Community, and LEED.
- Returning citizens – A pathway for the formerly incarcerated to re-enter the workforce.

- Veteran-friendly employer – A commitment to support returning service members' recruitment, training, and retention.
- Welfare to career – A program that guides people from welfare to a meaningful career also increases engagement and retention.
- Women's Business Enterprise – A project to improve supplier diversity in the supply chain.
- Young Professionals of Color Conference – From 2012 to 2020, the company held an event in West Michigan that provided business advice to those of color that was career-changing and inspirational.

Cascade Engineering commits to the extended community beyond the walls of its plant operations.

REVITALIZING DEINDUSTRIALIZED COMMUNITIES

The deindustrialization of communities in the latter portion of the 20th century left many cities and towns dealing with former manufacturing sites contaminated by hazardous substances, a loss of tax revenue, less earning power, increased social issues, and decaying infrastructure. However, the manufacturing sector can play a role in revitalizing communities that collectively better regions and the world. Key elements of the High-Roads Industrial Commons[17] include:

1. "retains, restores, and establishes new globally competitive advanced manufacturing and related industrial businesses;
2. retains, restores, and creates family-sustaining jobs for dislocated, incumbent, and young workers;
3. promotes social inclusion and creates economic opportunities for minorities and low-income families to increase their economic and social mobility;
4. targets all left behind, struggling communities and their residents, regardless of race, ethnicity, age, gender, or

geographical locales (that is, rural, urban, and suburban communities suffering from economic distress);

5. emphasize collaboration and partnerships between critical federal, state, and local government agencies and programs, as well as business, labor, academic, non-governmental, and not-for-profit actors and stakeholders engaged in the commons; and

6. Strengthening linkages, breaking down silos, and supporting coordination across the commons activities."

I propose adopting the extensive details of the model at the local, regional, state, national, and international levels. This work would allow for better communities utilizing all the previous humanist commitments that emphasize social awareness of the neighborhoods in which we operate. We can then use our unique capabilities to create thriving in the internal and external circles of influence impacted by our manufacturing operations and in partnership with other industry organizations. Additionally, they share examples of areas that have succeeded in this approach: the Akron, OH area around polymers, and Albany, NY, around semiconductors. The key players were the company research activities, research universities, community colleges, local government authorities, and start-ups.

CLOSING COMMENTS

Adopting the humanist commitments from Chapter 2 is a first step in developing thriving communities where all citizens can, at a minimum, meet their needs while having the opportunity to maximize their full potential. Other topics that benefit the local community and beyond are responsible actions like circular design, eliminating harmful materials or processes, and operating manufacturing sites with zero environmental harm. A favorite topic is creating employment opportunities for highly underemployed employees despite having superior work capabilities. The suggestions can work based on the successes of many manufacturers in hiring individuals from these alternative employment pools. Like many chapters in this book, we are just scratching the surface of many approaches to creating thriving communities.

CHAPTER REFLECTION QUESTIONS

Does a current or future employment gap exist for your organization?

Are you willing to explore opportunities to fill the gap with segments of the employment pool that you had not previously considered?

What can you do internally?

Is the environment in your area open to collaboration to develop and manage programs to help those in need of an opportunity to succeed?

Are you living in a deindustrialized community that needs to be revitalized?

RECOMMENDED READING

Independent Thinking on Restorative Practice: Building relationships, improving behavior and creating stronger communities (2021) – Mark Finnis – Independent Thinking Press

Mastering Community: The Surprising Ways Coming Together Moves Us from Surviving to Thriving (2022) – Christine Porath – Balance

The Local Economy Solution: How innovative, Self-financing "Pollinator" Enterprises Can Grow Jobs and Prosperity (2015) – Michael H. Shuman – Chelsea Green Publishing

PHASE 6

**STRATEGY,
PLANNING, CHANGE**

6. Develop a strategy,
determine the tactical steps,
and plan the change
management process.

The final phase of the Humanist Manufacturing Framework is when planning begins to move the company from the current state to a more human-centered future state operation. The planning team can build on the content of the book. Additionally, I encourage those participating in this work to do further research. In particular, in their discipline areas, since what has been shared in the book only scratches the surface of a tremendous wealth of knowledge on manufacturing best practices. The best plans will emerge from a team where all members have done a deep dive into what is available.

The work starts by shifting conversations from a deficit basis to a strengths-based approach necessary to drive the beneficial change essential to achieve organizational transformational results. A shift in our dialogue with others from a deficit to a strengths-based approach is required to drive the beneficial change necessary to achieve organizational transformational results. I have experienced success in adopting this process in a manufacturing setting.

Once the shift in the approach to conversations occurs, the company will begin by developing a strategy using the SOAR Framework, "an innovative, strengths-based whole system approach to strategic planning … which invites the whole system (stakeholders) into the process." The objective is to determine strategic initiatives to carry out the "why," vision, mission, and values.

Next, a well-developed strategy requires the work to determine the tactical plans necessary to achieve the strategic initiatives. The leadership team will lead the organization from strategic planning to tactical development plans. Executive champions are assigned from the leadership teams that would assemble a tactical team to develop the high-level Opportunity implementation plan. Various sub-teams then receive assignments at different levels of the organization with subgoal statements for their unit. All of the Opportunities need to be integrated across the organization.

The phase ends with the development of the change management process. Internal and external stakeholders, at a minimum, representatives of each group, if not all members, should have routinely received communications about the ongoing work. However, this may be the first opportunity for some individuals, groups, and the entire organization to learn how the evolving future state will impact them. A well-crafted and executed change management plan is necessary to realize the "why" and vision.

CHAPTER 12
DEVELOPING THE COMPANY STRATEGY

"SOAR has become a mainstay for organizations and communities wanting a way forward that engages everyone along a mutually agreed path."

—Jackie Stavros

Upon reaching this point in the book, the reader has had the opportunity to explore many ways to become a more human-centered manufacturing operation. As a result, a deeper understanding of how manufacturing can be a force for good inside the plant, community, and beyond is available. With this expanded knowledge, the next phase is to engage representatives of the organization's stakeholder groups in strategic planning, tactical planning, and the change processes. Again, the participants should use the "why," vision, mission, and values to guide their work through the various phases. The opportunity to maximize success in the strategic planning process is to set the stage for conversations that promote meaningful engagement.

BEGIN WITH A SHIFT IN CONVERSATIONS

We explored the need to focus on the positive and the benefits we derive from that approach. Better conversations are critical to the success of integrating greater emphasis on positivity in our relationships. A shift in our dialogue with others from a deficit basis to a strengths-based approach is necessary to drive the beneficial change essential to achieve transformational results for an organization. "Conversation is a crucial part of everything we do" is the basis of the book *Conversations Worth Having: Using Appreciative Inquiry to Fuel Productive and Meaningful Engagement.*[1] The nature of conversations should be appreciative, achieved by using an inquiry-based approach to generate information and statement-based affirmative interactions with the intent to add value.

To generate conversations worth having is a three-step process of:

1. Name It - Identifying an unwanted problem or complaint.
2. Flip It – Determining the positive opposite.
3. Frame It – What do you desire as the favorable outcome or impact.

I have experienced success in adopting this process in a manufacturing setting. Continuing the earlier example, I faced a plant where none of the production lines had ever made their daily production rate. We were also experiencing high scrap numbers and downtime. So that was the *Name It* step. I could have chosen to ask what they were doing wrong and why they were not doing more to reach their targets. I instead *Flipped It* and began to write positive notes on the whiteboards with the production data found at the end of each manufacturing line. Some days early on, finding something positive was more difficult than others. I knew they were paying attention to them as I was occasionally away from the plant. They would ask the next day why I had not written one. However, it was clear that they understood that we had *Framed It* where the desired impact was occurring.

In six months, almost every line in the plant hit its daily rate while significantly decreasing scrap and downtime. Line leaders would come to my office with a smile from ear to ear to tell me that they had "made rate" that day. A quality manager from our customer was in the plant one day and told me he did not know what we were doing, but he had never seen people that worked as hard as our employees. Of course, it was not the only reason for our success. Still, the overall positive approach across all conversations was the primary reason we saw a significant improvement in plant operations.

STRATEGIC PLANNING USING THE SOAR FRAMEWORK

I have long argued that leaders need to look out for 3-5 years to define a desired future state, conduct a current state evaluation of the organization, and then develop a plan to reach that North Star. While the general concept makes sense, the reality is that this work requires many incremental steps even to build the plan, let alone carry it to a successful outcome. The balance of this chapter is a strategic planning framework that has led to the development, execution, monitoring, and revision success of many organizations.

SOAR™ is an acronym for Strengths, Opportunities, Aspirations, and Results. A definition is "a strategic thinking, planning, conversations, and leading framework." This approach integrates Appreciative Inquiry (AI) with a strategic planning framework to create a transformational process that inspires organizations to SOAR™.[2]

Appreciative Inquiry[3] is a paradigm shift away from a deficit-based focus to one of positive, strengths-based change. The AI-4-D-Cycle begins with an affirmative topic around identifying a positive organizational core that leads to a "life-giving" story. There are four steps:

1. *Discovery – "What gives life?" The best of what is. Appreciating.*
2. *Dream – "What might be?" Envisioning. Results/Impact.*
3. *Design – "What should be – the ideal?" Co-constructing.*
4. *Destiny – "How to empower, learn, and improvise?" Sustaining.*

The SOAR™ framework for strategic inquiry and decision-making uses AI to bring stakeholder dialogue into strategic planning.

The SOAR™ framework goes beyond the SWOT model to link the internal strengths and external opportunities to the vision and mission of the organization, as well as to create strategic initiatives, strategy, tactical plans, and measurable results. The focus is on strengths and opportunities. We do not ignore weaknesses and threats but reframe them as opportunities. It seems like an irrelevant change in perspective, yet I have seen remarkable shifts in participant engagement through this positive lens. I would begin a planning session where people sat with folded arms and a 'why am I here' look on their faces. As our time together proceeded, they would start to lean in and participate fully. In most cases, it created the necessary breakthrough for the organizations I worked with to make the desired transformation.

SOAR™ accelerates the strategic planning efforts of an organization by focusing directly on those elements that will give life energy to the future, the organization's people. It is made explicit by dialogue between and among these groups of stakeholders.[4] Therefore, as the strategic planning process begins, it is an excellent time to revisit the initial "why," vision, mission, and values from the leadership team's previous work. These should guide but not constrain the work in the phases of the SOAR work seen in the balance of this chapter.

The first step is for the organization's leadership to determine if the SOAR framework is the approach to utilize in the initiate phase. It is crucial to establish the guidelines that will be used and to gain buy-in before the planning work begins by committing to:

- Following an approach that focuses on strengths.
- Seeking to understand the whole system with the voices of all relevant stakeholders, both internal and external to the organization.
- Centering on what an organization is doing right.
- Defining what skills to enhance.
- Determining what is compelling to those with a stake in the organization's success.

The guidelines have been essential for many successful strategic planning sessions across various industries.

INQUIRY INTO ORGANIZATIONAL STRENGTHS

The SOAR strategy development and formulation approach begins with an inquiry into strengths. In this case, we orchestrate questions using appreciative dialogue.[5] Practical examination for strategic planning includes explicit consideration of the organization's purpose – its mission, the customers it serves, and the stakeholders it impacts. This inquiry enables participants to examine, clarify, and consciously evolve their desired purpose and commitment to themselves and their organization.

Beginning the planning work with a focus on strengths reinforces the positive perspective crucial to maximizing the ability of the team to realize an ideal future state. The organization's current state can sometimes make this difficult if it lives in a deficit-based state. The intelligent person tasked with leading the planning process will have done the homework to help the planning team tease out existing strengths.

The following questions are examples of questions to guide the Strengths conversations:[6]

- *What are we most proud of as an organization? How does that reflect our most significant strength?*
- *What makes us unique? What can we be best at in our world?*
- *What is our proudest achievement in the last year or two?*
- *What does that tell us about our ability to use our strengths to get results?*
- *How do our strengths fit with the realities of the marketplace?*
- *What is world-class we currently provide for our clients, customers, industry, and other potential stakeholders?*

My experience is that it is good to break up those in the meeting into smaller groups to begin answering these questions. Ideally, the teams would be distributed based on their personality profiles to balance each group's perspectives. Then, as it appears that they finish answering them, I pull the entire group back together to do a round-robin where each team shares one answer at a time. I usually record these on a flip chart and indicate if more than one team has the same answer. The process continues until each group has shared its list of answers.

I then lead a conversation around what are common themes that have emerged. We will also discuss the answers that could benefit from further exploration. There will be a desire by some to begin to shift to 'a strength is _____, but' with the intent to turn it into an organizational weakness. It is vital to stop them politely, and I usually use humor to contain the intention to introduce negativity into the conversation. As the work culminates, there should be a solid understanding of the current organizational strengths. It usually also increases the pride of the participants in their company.

IMAGINING THE OPPORTUNITIES

The imagine phase is where stakeholders collectively explore known opportunities, hoping to discover more through stakeholder dialogue. This phase aims to have stakeholder input into opportunities that will be given consideration when developing short and long-term goals and creating the overall strategy. This phase also identifies the organization's shared value set, vision, and mission through opportunities for stakeholders to activate effective strategy formulation.[7]

The following questions are examples of questions to guide the Opportunities conversation:[8]

- *How do we make sense of opportunities provided by the external forces and trends?*
- *What are the top three opportunities on which we should focus our efforts?*
- *How can we best meet the needs of our stakeholders, including clients, customers, employees, shareholders, and the community?*
- *Who are possible new clients and customers?*
- *How can we distinctively differentiate ourselves from existing or potential competitors?*
- *What are potential new markets, products, services, or processes?*
- *How can we reframe challenges into exciting opportunities?*

- *Include those related to sustainability and regenerative business; what new skills do we need to move forward?*

During this imagine phase, I encourage participants to close their eyes and visualize the perfect work environment. What are people wearing? Where are they doing the work? How are coworkers interacting with one another? Are they proud of their impact on their customers and the community? Is there joy throughout the company? Does work carry over into their personal lives in a positive manner? As shared in the first chapter's opening, are they excited to go to work each day to further benefit the world?

It is crucial to do extensive research to fully leverage our opportunities to understand our organizational challenges, industry sector, business in general, and society. My experience has been that participants limit themselves to what they currently know. An effective scan requires a comprehensive look at current and future forces, issues, and trends to flesh out a complete set of opportunities fully.

STRATEGIES AND PLANS TO REACH OUR ASPIRATIONS

Aspirations emerge in the innovation phase with calls to co-construct the most preferred future. With these transformational factors taken into consideration, organizations can create a new future and sustain a sense of commitment and urgency over a long period. This phase also involves the design of strategies and tactics to support the new business model. The following chapters will look into this in more detail. First, however, examples of Aspiration questions include:[9]

- *When exploring our values and aspirations, "what are we deeply passionate about?"*
- *Reflecting on our Strengths and Opportunities conversations, who are we, who should we become, and where should we go in the future?*
- *What is our most compelling aspiration?*

- *What strategic initiatives (i.e., projects, programs, and processes) support our aspirations?*

Like guidance for brainstorming, the group should allow all participants to share their responses to all questions listing reactions on a flip chart. The exercise should be free-flowing and done without passing judgment during this initial phase. The objective is to gain an overall sense of what is essential to individuals in the group. Others may not have considered some thoughts that may emerge, yet once voiced, it creates an immediate consensus of being an aspirational element to adopt.

MONITORING AND CONTINUALLY IMPROVING OUR RESULTS

Finally, the implementation phase is where employees are inspired through authentic recognition and reward to act on the shared plans to achieve measurable Results. When the SOAR framework is successful, the energy and momentum created in the previous phases inspire the participants to complete the necessary actions to achieve the desired outcomes. Teams develop meaningful and measurable goals with feedback measures to monitor the progress towards the results. Course corrections evolve as new information or shifts that impact the earlier strategic objectives emerge.

The assembled strategic planning team would consider the following questions as they determine how to track their Results:[10]

- *Considering our Strengths, Opportunities, and Aspirations, what meaningful measures would indicate that we are on track to achieving our goals?*
- *What are 3 to 5 indicators that would create a scorecard that addresses a triple bottom line of profits, people, and the planet?*
- *What resources are needed to implement our most vital projects?*
- *What are the best rewards to support those who achieve our goals?*

The group will define the lowest level for monitoring their Results assignments. Ideally, these will be driven down to the level where individuals have the most significant opportunity to impact the Results. An example could be manufacturing processes using utilities like electricity and water. First, the groups can set a baseline for current usage. Next, they would begin developing and implementing initiatives to help achieve the desired goals. Finally, if multiple areas or shifts were doing similar work, combine the numbers to show the overall success in achieving the desired Results.

CLOSING COMMENTS

Isern and Pung[11] offer support for the viability of the SOAR™ framework. They found that urgent challenges require a transformative engine that creates digestible themes. These themes attain high aspirations through stakeholder dialogue when they are made relevant and communicated compellingly.

Companies should constantly scan the manufacturing environment to determine where their current products are on the life cycle. For example, the Hoover Harness and Leather Goods Factory bought the patent[12] for the vacuum cleaner in the early 1900s. The automotive industry was on the rise, and likely someone at Hoover saw the need to pivot their organization away from horse-drawn buggies.

A current significant transition we are experiencing is the shift from internal combustion engines to an all-electric future recently announced by GM,[13] with others also on that path. It will be essential to consider the impact of an aging and unstable electrical grid[14] and the need to put environmental policies in place to deal with the issues of battery raw materials[15] and end-of-life battery waste.[16] The shift in electric vehicle power plants will also impact the petroleum industry. If done correctly, a significant opportunity for environmental benefit will affect many different sectors in the coming decades.

A strategic planning team successfully navigating the SOAR framework has realized a significant accomplishment. The organization has reached this point with a deep understanding of the Strengths, Opportunities, Aspirations, and Results necessary to generate transformational change. The work now shifts from higher-level strategy to developing tactical plans to prepare for the eventual rollout of the change process.

CHAPTER REFLECTION QUESTIONS

Is the company culture one of positivity and holistic engagement that includes all internal and external key stakeholders?

Is strategic planning done using an innovative, strengths-based whole-systems process?

Are all critical stakeholders invited to the strategic planning process?

Are the evolving plans compelling to those with a stake in the organization's success?

How does the adoption of humanist commitments align with your thoughts on the content of this chapter?

RECOMMENDED READING

Conversations Worth Having: Using Appreciative Inquiry to Fuel Productive and Meaningful Engagement (2018) – Jackie Stavros & Cheri Torres – Berrett-Koehler Publishers, Inc.

Thin Book of SOAR: Creating Strategy That Inspires Innovation and Engagement (2021) – Jackie Stavros & Gina Hinrichs – The SOAR Institute, www.soar-strategy.com

CHAPTER 13
THE IMPORTANCE OF
TACTICAL PLANS

*"Strategy without tactics is the slowest route to victory. Tactics
without strategy is the noise before defeat."*

—Sun Tzu

With a robust strategic plan that positions them to move from the
status quo to new heights of performance, the company has realized an
integral step to achieving its vision. The next step is to develop the
tactical plans necessary to carry out the strategy. First, the strategic
planning team members should revisit the "why," vision, mission, and
values. Has anything come out of the SOAR planning process where
these need refinement? If so, these changes should occur before
moving forward. Once this assessment is complete, the work begins to
develop the tactical plans.

As Sun Tzu states, strategy is an idea and an unfulfilled vision
without proper tactical plans. Therefore, the work to transform the
organization continues by breaking down the high-level Opportunities
from the SOAR process into smaller ones. The planning group will
eventually share tactical plans across the various business units and

departments that collectively integrate the different building blocks to achieve the higher-level objectives.

THE TACTICAL PLANNING PROCESS

The leadership team would begin moving from strategic planning to developing tactical plans. The group would assign an executive champion responsible for one or more of the strategic Opportunities resulting from the SOAR planning process that will allow the organization to begin the path toward reaching its Aspirations. The executive drafts a goal statement for their assigned Opportunity. Then each group member shares them with the balance of the executive team for feedback and uses that input for further refinement of each goal statement until agreeable to all executive team members. The goal statement will guide the project, and the team can display them prominently throughout the life of the project. Defining and monitoring goal statements is an essential focus, as I have seen scope creep occur when the team loses focus on the initial objective.

At this level, the executive team would benefit from using the Baldrige Excellence Framework[1] factors of approach, deployment, learning, and integration (ADLI) to fully develop the various tasks necessary to effectively and efficiently implement the assigned strategy. The result is the development of a holistic project plan to address the following for each of the Opportunities:

Approach comprises:

- *the methods used to carry out the process,*
- *the appropriateness of these methods to the item questions and your operating environment,*
- *the effectiveness of your use of the methods, and*
- *the degree to which the approach is repeatable and based on reliable data and information (i.e., systematic).*

Deployment is the extent to which:

- *your approach addresses item questions that are relevant and important to your organization,*
- *your approach is applied consistently, and*
- *your approach is used by all appropriate work units.*

Learning comprises:

- *the refinement of your approach through cycles of evaluation and improvement,*
- *the adoption of best practices or innovations to improve your approach, and*
- *the sharing of refinements and innovations with other relevant work units and processes in your organization.*

Integration is the extent to which:

- *your approach is aligned with the organizational needs,*
- *your measures, information, and improvement systems are complementary across processes and work units; and*
- *your plans, processes, results, analyses, learning, and actions are harmonized across processes and work units to support organization-wide goals.*

It would be essential that the executive team work together to understand what is necessary to develop an optimal approach, deploy it efficiently and effectively, and realize the end goal of a complete set of fully integrated Opportunities. However, the work does not end at that point, as it is essential to have a learning process that leads to continuous improvement.

DEVELOPING THE TACTICAL TEAMS

The executive champion would assemble a tactical team to develop the high-level Opportunity implementation plan. The membership of this team should continue the SOAR framework practice of stakeholder representation from those impacted by the project. In addition, there would be representatives from the various project sub-teams. Finally, other internal and external stakeholders affected by the project or individuals who could provide additional support would receive an invitation to join. Once the executive team defines the goal statements for each strategic opportunity, they need to identify measures that will help track the organization's success.

Various sub-teams then receive assignments at different levels of the organization with subgoal statements for their unit. An example of an Opportunity is to improve employee engagement. The president might be the executive champion for the overall improvement. A sub-team could be assigned to the manufacturing management group responsible for improving employee engagement in that business unit. Further division of the project can be subgroups of maintenance, materials, production, and quality groups. More extensive operations may include teams from each shift in the subgroups.

After setting up the executive champion, high-level team, and various sub-teams, they define the best strategies to accomplish the assigned Opportunity. The project teams will do an internal and external assessment of the current state of the operation using the goal statement as their guide. Continuing the employee engagement example, the high-level team would research the topic to see what others in their industry and other sectors had done to improve employee engagement. They could look for articles, case studies, implementation guides, training providers, and companies specializing in the topic area.

The high-level team might select a survey that will be used at all levels to develop a baseline for the current status of employee engagement. The data analysis can identify the areas of concern to determine the strategies, innovations, and projects required to pursue each strategic opportunity to improve employee engagement. All information is available at each project team level.

The sub-teams would be allowed to self-organize around each goal area whenever possible. Allowing individuals to select the Opportunities of significant interest will lead to a more committed team. The sub-team members would plan actions and gain individual and collaborative commitments for their area of responsibility. They would use the defined strategies from the high-level team as their guide to moving toward the goal statement as defined by the executive champion and agreed upon by the executive team.

An assessment of each team participant and the team determines their needs for capacity development. The high-level team would be responsible for providing support, resources, and training to ensure success in realizing the defined goal statement objectives. The high-level team would also identify integration linkages between the goal areas in their overall scope of responsibility. Finally, using a color-coded approach to monitor the work of each of the groups allows the high-level team to help as necessary to enable the sub-teams to improvise, innovate and re-inquire the action plans.

VISUAL MANAGEMENT

I am a visual person who wants to spend as little time as possible monitoring projects. As a plant manager, I could assess the entire operation in about ten minutes by looking through all the visual indicators in a well-set-up plant operation. Color-coding is a similar tool to visualize the project status of the associated tasks quickly. Those shaded as green indicate moving forward per the schedule. If one stumbles, it will be yellow, demonstrating that the project team has an action plan to get things back on track. Red projects need attention outside the core group to get them back on track. Using this format allows a nearly instant overall status of the projects. In the employee engagement example, the executive champion could use this to monitor overall success in the work to achieve this objective.

I also like the analogy of an onion approach to tactical project management. The outside layer of the onion is the high-level project team with the overall responsibility to achieve the goal statement for each Opportunity. As you peel back each layer, the project is broken down into smaller sub-teams, as previously mentioned. The size of the project will determine how many layers are needed to track tasks at a level that does not become too granular. For example, imagine an organizational chart where one can quickly see a high-level project is yellow, which may jeopardize the completion date. The executive champion and the high-level project team can peel back layers drilling down to the root cause that put the project into yellow. Knowing this detail in the week when making adjustments to the schedule should allow everyone to react to ensure project success. The high-level color status would be the lowest color level of any sub-team. If at least one sub-team is yellow, the overall project is yellow, or if any are red, the project is red.

A leadership team that actively monitors the projects will be able to gauge overall performance against the plan. The reality is that projects will need adjustments to the initial plan as they progress. The key is that when this occurs, the project team adjusts their work appropriately and communicates this to everyone in the weekly update. This ongoing interaction should never surprise anyone that a project has significantly gone off the rails. Projects must not go red for overall successful organizational operations achievement. More importantly, the leadership should not have their faces go red and smoke rolling out of their ears when this might occur.

I endorse an approach to openly sharing project updates from the initial development through completion. The teams will set the various tasks, start and end dates, and assigned resources. Each plan is accessible for viewing by all members of the organization. Once the project begins, each team would update the status on an agreed-upon day of the week. Then anyone from an entry-level position to top leadership can track project performance. The color-coded approach takes just a few seconds to scan how well things are progressing. The desired result is no unforeseen surprises and individuals doing their work as planned.

PROJECT MANAGEMENT

Organizations looking to implement transformational strategies will benefit by building their approach laid out earlier in this chapter within a formal project management process. The benefit of effective project management is the timely completion of the tactical plans through effective and efficient use of the organization's resources.

The overall success in implementing the Opportunities from the strategic plan is centralized coordination. Keeping the work and goals in one place ensures that available personnel are not under or over-utilized. In addition, communication alignment supports working in a coordinated manner, resulting in more significant potential for overall success.

Project success requires breaking down tasks to the lowest level with each action that needs to occur. The project plan is more substantial with collective input from all team members. Attention to detail must be emphasized as missing one task can later cause the project to go off the rails. An example is the failure to order a long lead time part promptly.

The key project management elements are:

- Project scope – The team works from a well-defined expectation of the overall criteria for a successful project. To avoid scope creep, the scope should be front and center throughout the project. If the scope needs to expand, an update to the document should record the change officially.
- Budget – The allocation of available funds to carry out each task.
- Intelligent goals – Establish clear metrics and criteria to measure project success accurately.
- Project plan – A Gantt chart is a specific tool to develop a project plan with the overall start and end dates, a list of all tasks, when the tasks begin and end, the budgeted time it will take to accomplish the tasks, the persons responsible for completing the tasks, the required resources, and milestones. The task dependencies identification is vital to project success as well.

A well-developed plan provides the best opportunity for completing the project on time. In addition, the above simplifies essential skills that a professional project planner brings to the work.

Employing those with the talents and skills to do this work is critical to project success.

When thinking about the level of attention to detail for successful projects, I think of my dad. At one point in his career, he was responsible for developing the computer numerical control (CNC) machine programs in the shop where he worked. He commented that if he missed one step in the program, there was potential for a crash that could cause machine or part damage. Worse yet, it might cause an injury to the operator. Project planning is much the same; every detail must be part of the comprehensive list of all necessary tasks.

CLOSING COMMENTS

Tactical plans are essential in helping an organization achieve the identified Opportunities necessary to transform the company. Achievement of the goal statements has higher potential when the organization provides an environment that allows the various teams to succeed. The leadership team must commit to making the strategic plan a living inquiry process, continually aligning strength with opportunity in service of the future you most want to create.

CHAPTER REFLECTION QUESTIONS

Can all executive staff members be project team champions to carry out goal statements?

Are employees successful members of high-level and sublevel project teams with a clear sense and proper resources to implement strategic opportunities?

Are teams able to self-organize around goals?

Are action plans developed & collective commitments in place?

Has the company ensured capacity development and that all necessary resources are available?

Is the organization committed to the strategic plan?

How does the adoption of humanist commitments align with your thoughts on the content of this chapter?

RECOMMENDED READING

A Guide to the Project Management Body of Knowledge (PMBOKr Guide) and The Standard for Project Management (PMBOK® Guide) 7th Edition (2021) – Project Management Institute – Independent Publishers Group

Project Requirements: A Guide to Best Practices (2006) – Ralph R. Young – Management Concepts

CHAPTER 14
THE CHANGE PROCESS

"I alone cannot change the world, but I can cast a stone across the waters to create many ripples."

—MOTHER TERESA

In a typical case of opposites attracting, my wife and I are opposites regarding tolerance for change. My high achiever mode has my mind in a constant "what's next" manner where I generally see change as desirable. My wife prefers that if something is good, then change is unnecessary. Her perspective is in alignment with many members of our companies. Routine can be comforting. It was not immediately apparent that this was the case for my colleagues. It was vital for me to understand that others are less willing to adopt unknown change.

During my doctorate coursework, an assignment was to read the *Leading Change* book by Harvard Professor Dr. John Kotter, a recognized global expert on change leadership. The content of the book strongly resonated with me. His eight-step process for effective and efficient change implementation had a simple elegance I deeply admired. You will read more about these steps in the balance of this chapter. I have also built in other content that I have found beneficial in understanding how to most efficiently and effectively implement change. For example, developing a highly desirable work culture will take multiple years, even in the best cases, so everyone involved must be adaptable and comfortable with ongoing change.

KOTTER'S CHANGE PROCESS

Recently the change process in Dr. Kotter's 1996 book has been updated into the *8 Steps to Accelerate Change eBook*.[1] The steps are now known as accelerators that include:

1. Create a sense of urgency.
2. Build a guiding coalition.
3. Form a strategic vision and initiatives.
4. Enlist a volunteer army.
5. Enable action by removing barriers.
6. Generate short-term wins.
7. Sustain acceleration.
8. Institute change.

You would expect nothing less from a change framework than to evolve to meet the world's increased pace. The business environment continues to move at an accelerating rate. The advances in technology we continue to see have made it possible to know what is happening around the globe in near real-time, creating a need for organizations to react nimbly to changes that can require a complete overnight reset of existing plans. The change process has impacts in the following ways:

- Change has moved from sequential and finite steps to a need for continuous and concurrent use of the accelerators.
- A shift from only a guiding coalition of key team members to an engagement of the entire organization committed to driving the necessary change.
- Moving from a traditional hierarchy to an agile, nimble network evolving as needs arise supported by the traditional leadership structure.

- Moving from a linear approach focused on a single initiative to quickly reacting to a constant scanning of relevant opportunities to implement for the organization's benefit.

Four change principles are essential to ensuring success in driving the desired change:

1. Leadership and management work together to lead the critical change initiatives aligned with the company vision. The work must flow using essential managerial processes.
2. Head and heart work seamlessly where logic alone is not enough. The current workforce desires to be part of a more significant cause. When individual meaning and purpose align, achieving extraordinary change is possible.
3. Utilize a select few in tandem with the many to realize impactful change. All members are not yet ready to carry out the improvement initiatives. However, those who have fully bought in can help others embed them into their collective DNA. Out of this work, unknown leaders will emerge at all levels of the organization that can be fully engaged to accelerate even more significant improvement.
4. The leadership must drive energy in the organization to shift members from a "Have To" to a "Want To" mindset.

Each organization must develop a sense of urgency that resonates with the desire of stakeholders to enthusiastically embrace the company's "why," vision, mission, and values. Once identified, the leadership team needs to develop a communication plan that articulates the identified opportunity to share the results from success and the consequences of failure. The work requires a delicate balance of "optimal tension."

AN IDEAL STATE OF URGENCY

Keeping an entire workforce at a heightened and ideal state of urgency is no simple task. The organization's leaders and managers will need to develop an honest and ongoing two-way dialogue to keep tuned to the overall condition of the employee base. Each of us has a point where we can perform at an optimal level where individual and teamwork are not allowed to slip. Yet there is enough optimal tension to stretch us beyond our current performance expectations without causing damage. Ultimately, we want to push them to a point where each member of the organization is performing at their peak and then weaving everyone together to reach the maximum full potential of the entire unit.

THE GUIDING COALITION

The next step is the selection and assessment of a guiding leadership coalition. The group's success improves by including the representation of critical stakeholders. Ideally, the people identified as members of the guiding alliance should consist of at least a subset of those involved in the SOAR work. The background knowledge of that work will improve the effectiveness and efficiency of the change process. At the same time, other individuals may be appropriate additions during the change process phase of the business transformation.

The process evaluates the coalition members for their instinctive, intellectual, intuitive, and rational characteristics. A similar version of the assessment and development plans for the organization's executive team can guide the work to assemble and develop an optimal leadership coalition. A training plan and the assignment of existing or the hiring of key personnel will address critical gaps in the capabilities of the guiding leadership coalition. As a result, the group will have more significant potential to ensure success in moving the firm's employee balance toward the vision developed from a whole stakeholder perspective during the SOAR process. All coalition members will commit to what must be a clear, concise, and compelling "why" and vision.

After establishing the guiding coalition, the group needs to explore current and future forces, issues, and trends more deeply to fully understand the Opportunities defined during the SOAR process. The team involved should comprehensively evaluate the work to understand better how to best leverage existing and new technologies, advanced composites, and other emerging enhancements in the manufacturing sector. Finally, the group should invest proper time to clearly understand the potential to maximize the selection and implementation of initiatives to transform the company.

A successful change process is not possible without an adequately prepared guiding coalition. A key role is to evaluate the organization's current state to identify the organization's positive core. The group should determine the sum of the:

- Their unique strengths to leverage during the work to achieve the vision.
- Assets that currently exist.
- Resources of the current knowledge base, people, technology, and infrastructure.
- Networks mapping of critical horizontal and vertical business and governmental relationships.
- Capabilities of each department that support the needs of the desired change.
- Creative thought that will carry the organization into the future.

The guiding coalition would revisit the vision developed to date against the following information compiled:

- Adopt the existing "why" for a more compelling future vision.
- Review and revise, if necessary, the mission statement that commits members to carry forward the very best of the past and inspire and challenge the status quo.
- Revisit the existing list of core values and improve if necessary.

The guiding coalition would then spread the organization's existing or revised vision, mission statement, and values to all stakeholders.

VISION AND INITIATIVES

Successful communication of the defined vision to the organization's internal and external stakeholders is required. The coalition works together until they can explain the near-term and long-term future states in less than five minutes. Creating a mental image of what the organization will look like needs to convey how it improves the situation for all stakeholders. The visualization should include the state of the organization in three months, six months, one year, and three years. The plan needs to be shared often and in various communication forms. The message may require sharing it ten times in multiple formats to understand expectations completely.

Communication to the various stakeholder impacted by the changes should include:

How the changes impact them individually in the following ways:

- Physically – Are the planned changes less demanding or create a safer work environment for the employees. For example, installing assistive robotic devices would reduce fatigue and lessen the potential for injury.
- Mentally – What will now be required of them psychologically related to the new job requirements. An employee engagement program would help to improve job satisfaction.
- Financially – If there is success in implementing the desired organizational improvements, information should be shared about how it will impact the workforce members. Productivity improvements could lead to a bonus or gainsharing checks.

Use visual devices to show:

- The new facility layout – Set up a small portion of the plant to replicate the entire operation after fully implementing the planned transformation. For example, a sample production line uses lean manufacturing with 5S, kaizen, pull systems, and visual management.

- Simulations – Utilizing computer technology to create a model of the organization's future state.
- Performance indicators – Develop a set of measures to track plant performance to the strategic plan.

In *Chapter 5: Knowing Thy Executive Team*, I shared the concept of "cut the tail" related to change management. Our volunteer army should consist of those on the bell curve of the small percentage of the employees ready to embrace organizational change. These individuals will be selected internally at all company levels and across departments or divisions with an invitation to engage in the transformation process fully. Additionally, we should ask external stakeholders with initial buy-in to the transition to the new vision to participate as members of the change team. Finally, the volunteer army will work on compelling the balance of the employees to become additional members of this essential group. The large-scale change required to transform a company can only happen if a significant number of employees at all levels of the organization work in concert to drive the desired change.

ENLISTING A VOLUNTEER ARMY

I like Kotter's perspective on a volunteer army. I often recommend that individuals interested in developing leadership skills join a nonprofit comprised of volunteers who champion a cause that is important to them. If they can inspire and motivate those who receive nothing beyond satisfaction for doing good for others, they will learn skills to take this to the next level with paid employees.

The current workforce wants to move beyond surviving to a workplace that allows them to flourish, be happy, and have an opportunity for fulfillment. Therefore, a strategic plan that will enable individuals to build a life of meaning and purpose is necessary. A successful strategy will support actions required to remove barriers and recognize early short-term wins. Each organization member needs clearly defined objectives and goals, access to accurate data, and an environment of effective two-way non-judgmental communication from active and dynamic leadership engaged in the proactive review of planned targets. Done effectively, the collection of each individual's success in achieving their goals will result in the sustained incremental change needed to reach the long-term vision.

GMBC Healthcare CEO and president John Chessare advocates[2] the Act of Enrollment process where change agents need to:

- Engage the person in a dialogue about the need for change.
- Invite questions or concerns about the change.
- Ask for a commitment to working on the change.

He has found this to be an often-overlooked step where leaders do not allow employees a comfortable and safe environment where they can better understand what is being asked of the organization and individuals. However, doing so allows two-way dialogue to happen early in the change process, resulting in greater clarity throughout the workforce of what they will experience and an opportunity to provide insight into potential issues unknown to that point in the planning work.

ENABLING ACTION

My experience is that many leaders and managers do not understand the need for employee empowerment. If they do, there is a lack of understanding of what it means and how to create a culture that embraces this critical element of business success. When I have been the most successful as a leader are the times when I was in an environment allowing this to blossom. The empowerment of employees should include:

- Removing structural barriers.
- Providing needed training.
- Aligning systems to the vision.

- Dealing with troublesome managers, supervisors, or employees – Cut the tail.
- Effectively tap an enormous source of power by enabling the entire workforce.

The success of the strategic plan is to monitor the earlier defined Results. It will be essential to pay attention to whether the culture is becoming ingrained in the minds and actions of the organization. Additional focus is required to execute the various tasks with timeliness, proper resource allocation, and embracing responsibility. The guiding coalition must improvise, innovate, and re-inquire the action plans.

We continue the theme of the root cause of a lack of proper leadership and focus on the human aspect of all stakeholders impacted by their businesses from the introduction in *Chapter 2: The Humanist Perspective*. When this occurs, we need to understand the feeling our workforces will experience as change occurs, particularly if we attempt to create substantial change. With this in mind, building on the Act of Enrollment, the transformation plan should include:

New beginning
Understand the reasons for resistance:

- Loss of control – The disruption of a known routine.
- Uncertainty – Wondering if this will be a positive or negative experience.
- Lack of information – Many less desirable future states emerge in employees' minds as they imagine what could happen without knowing actual plans.
- Too different – A significant departure from what has been the norm.
- Loss of "face." – Seen as a reduction in respect or the potential for humiliation.
- Insufficient knowledge – Seeing a gap between current capabilities and those necessary to adapt to the organization's future state.

- Ripple effects – Knowing that dominos will fall as the change impacts others in the organization.
- Personal loss - What's In It For Me (WIIFM) is unknown.
- More work – Seen as adding on to a current feeling of already doing too much.
- Past resentment – Issues without past resolution or adverse outcomes in past change initiatives return to the surface.

Neutral zone — transition period.

- Anxiety rises, and motivation falls – Employee minds begin to imagine worst-case scenarios that paralyze them.
- Absenteeism rises, and productivity falls – Calling out while finding other ways to numb the negative sense of the change or spending more time trying to figure out what is happening hampers getting the ongoing work done.
- Old weaknesses and past resentments resurface – Anything without past resolution continues to fester, both spoken and unspoken.
- Personnel is overloaded, and turnover increases – Mental and physical concerns augment the normal workload, and some employees will decide to move on.
- People become polarized - The majority of the workforce is in a state where they have to decide if they follow those on the far right of the bell curve embracing change or those on the far left that will fight plans at all costs.
- The organization is vulnerable – The leadership and the guiding coalition must work diligently to show the majority of the organization that the change will be ultimately beneficial.

Ending — leave the past behind.
How the employee's behavior and attitudes need to change – Resistance is a natural human response, but the members must commit to the organization's plans at some point.

- Sell the opportunity to them – The leadership must develop a communication plan that honestly and ethically explains the overall benefits of the strategies to improve the organization while simultaneously being upfront about any negative consequences.
- Why there is a need to change – Helping the employees clearly understand the company's internal and external pressures with the rationale for the transition plans.
- Create that sense of urgency – Setting expectations for the need to move forward to achieve necessary milestones promptly.

Enabling successful action takes great patience and understanding from the leadership and guiding coalition. In addition, these individuals need to embrace the need to be sensitive to the impact of change on the workforce. Finally, teaching the organization members about the benefits of the change through supportive and caring conversations will help everyone make smoother transitions when they can express their concerns in an environment of trust and cooperation.

SHORT-TERM WINS AND SUSTAINING ACCELERATION

Developing a transformation plan that generates a sense of possibility is essential. The workforce majority is teetering between following those who embrace the transition and those trying to maintain the status quo. Therefore, it is imperative to establish a positive environment where success occurs early and often. The following rules guide transformation success:

Ensure quick successes – Set a stage for early and regular wins.

People are reassured – A snowball effect occurs as initial small positive results build upon one another, accelerating the pace of change.

Restores morale and increases confidence - The past anxiety falls, and motivation rises as success begets success.

Celebrate success.

Mark and celebrate the ending of the old system – The organization pays proper homage to the past, recognizing the value of what was once critical to success.

Mark and celebrate the beginning of the new birth – It is essential to define the point where the launch begins towards attaining the transformational vision.

Celebrate early and often to:

- Recognize early successes – Helping the workforce see where they accomplish the necessary change.
- Reinforce desired behaviors – Focusing on the positive improvements and using others as an opportunity for learning.
- Remind people of the value of the new beginning – Continuing to communicate the benefits of the plan outcomes to company stakeholders.

As the transformation continues, the guiding coalition should work to consolidate gains and produce further change by:

- Using increased credibility to change all systems, structures, and policies that do not fit together and do not fit the transformation vision.
- Hiring, promoting, and developing people who can implement the change vision.
- Reinvigorating the process with new projects, themes, and change agents.

The guiding coalition needs to work to anchor the new approaches into the culture by:

- Creating better performance through customer and productivity-oriented behavior, better leadership, and more effective management.
- Articulating the connections between new behaviors and organizational success.
- Developing plans to ensure leadership development and succession.

ESSENTIAL ELEMENTS TO CONSIDER

I recommend that those desiring to make a significant manufacturing transformation should embed the following key elements into their organization:

1. Accountability – Create an environment where the workforce has proper resources with clear expectations for timely and successful completion of assignments.
2. Discipline – Train employees to obey the organization's code of conduct.
3. Rewarding goal progress – Distribute proper benefits for successful work.
4. Recognition of goal achievement - Provide appropriate acknowledgment for accomplishing initiatives in their area of responsibility.
5. Clearly defined objectives and goals – Balance the need for autonomy, innovation, and creativity with the ability to provide clear expectations.
6. Accurate data – Build a robust information gathering system that enhances the potential for project success based on facts.
7. Effective two-way non-judgmental communication – Creating a culture that encourages supportive dialogue and appropriate input from all stakeholders.

8. Active and dynamic leadership – Regular and positive interaction at all company levels where leaders experience what those in all departments face while carrying out their assignments.
9. Policy deployment – Build a framework that efficiently and effectively links all organization members' work.
10. Proactive review of planned targets – Establish regular evaluation intervals to ensure transformation progress and the ability to respond to ongoing challenges.
11. Common knowledge of philosophy and mechanics of change management – Educate everyone on the various aspects of moving the organization from the current state to the future vision.
12. Clearly defined roles – Develop job descriptions that align with organizational needs while eliminating gaps or unnecessary duplications.
13. Attention to detail – Complete a mental checklist that walks through every project phase to ensure no surprises that add additional costs or time delays.
14. Heavy plan – Light do – Spend appropriate time in the initial development of implementation plans, leading to more favorable project outcomes.
15. Willingness to occasionally fail while taking calculated risks – Develop a culture that encourages intelligent risk-taking that understands that pushing the boundaries will lead to learning when experiencing less favorable outcomes but collectively enhances organizational capabilities.
16. Listen effectively to the voice of the customer – Spend time asking questions of the customer base in the actual environments where they use company products and services.
17. Commitment to the employees – Apply the humanist commitments from *Chapter 2: Humanist Perspective*.
18. Active consideration of stakeholders – Again, apply the humanist perspectives to the betterment of all company partners.

The list is not all-inclusive but provides additional insight into the work that needs to move forward to achieve the desired vision.

INSTITUTING CHANGE

Ultimately, the leadership and guiding coalition need to put in the necessary work to put the organization on a successful trajectory. An organization should consider this chapter's content to develop and execute a change management plan properly. In particular, giving appropriate consideration to the human element of the company. The work would move the organization from a traditional one of:

- Orders are dictated to the organization, where responsibility resides at the highest levels.
- Personnel frustrated because of limited opportunities for involvement – "They don't listen to us."
- Little or no communication about company goals and performance.
- Barriers to personal and professional satisfaction.
- Boundaries between functions and inefficiencies prevail.

Instead, an organization fully utilizes its positive core and strengths of:

- Decisions are made at the lowest possible level.
- Personnel involved, committed, and proudly participating with a sense of belonging.
- Continuous pursuit of perfection and waste elimination.
- Extensive communication about company goals and performance.
- Work provides personal and professional satisfaction.
- No boundaries between functions.

Most people in an organization want to contribute to the company's betterment. In particular, if they are motivated by a compelling "why" and vision.

CLOSING COMMENTS

A successful company defines strategic initiatives, designs coordinated and targeted activities, and executes them with urgency to make transformational vision achievement possible. The end objective is a vision that presents a desirable and straightforward verbal picture we can easily communicate so that employees can imagine it as feasible and desirable. Additionally, it integrates with a timelessness that allows for flexibility as the organization evolves. If so, the organization will have more significant potential for success.

CHAPTER REFLECTION QUESTIONS

Has a sense of urgency for change been achieved?

Who will be the members of the guiding coalition?

Have the strategic vision and initiatives been sufficiently communicated?

Have you enlisted a volunteer army of employees to participate in the transformation process?

Have you enabled action by removing barriers?

Are you able to generate short-term wins?

Is their commitment to sustain change acceleration?

Is the organization capable of transformative change?

How does the adoption of humanist commitments align with your thoughts on the content of this chapter?

RECOMMENDED READING

Change (the) Management: Why We as Leaders Must Change for the Change to Last (2020) – Al Comeaux – Lioncrest Publishing

Leading Change (2012) – John P. Kotter – Harvard Business Review Press – Hachette Book Group

Managing Transitions: Making the Most of Change (2017) – William Bridges and Susan Bridges

Our Iceberg Is Melting: Changing and Succeeding Under Any Conditions (2006) – John Kotter and Holger Rathgeber – St. Martin's Press

CONCLUSION
WRAPPING IT UP

"We have a choice to make during our brief visit to this beautiful blue and green living planet: to hurt it or to help it."

—Ray Anderson

We came in with Ray Anderson in the first chapter and will close with him. Although I never met the man, he has impacted my life in ways I would have never expected. He is one of my few heroes. Since he has departed this earth, I will never know, but I believe he would not object to supporting most of this book's content. His work led to his legacy as a pioneer of corporate sustainability, which inspired a significant pivot in my journey. I am eternally grateful to him and many others for leaving or living a humanist manufacturing legacy. Ray and others profiled in this book have led me to choose the "help it" option from his quote, where I hope to enlist manufacturers to reverse the damage done to our "beautiful blue and green living planet."

After a conversation on their plans to become a sustainable manufacturer to an Interface group in California in March of 1996, Anderson returned home to Atlanta. Five days later, he knew that he had reached at least one person, Glen C. Thomas, who wrote the following poem:

Tomorrow's Child

Without a name; an unseen face
and knowing not your time nor place,
Tomorrow's Child, though yet unborn
I met you first last Tuesday morn.

A wise friend introduced us two,
and through his shining point of view
I saw a day that you would see;
a day for you, but not for me.

Knowing you has changed my thinking
for I never had an inkling
That perhaps the things I do
might someday, somehow, threaten you.

Tomorrow's Child, my daughter / son
I'm afraid I've just begun
To think of you and of your good,
though always having known I should.

Begin I will to weigh the cost
of what I squander; what is lost
If ever I forget that you
will someday come to live here too.

You can hear Tomorrow's Child[1] read by Anderson. His reading of this poem was a significant part of my sustainability epiphany.

Ray Anderson's move to shape the business practices of Interface through a sustainability lens ignited a purpose in my life to use business as a force for good. His approach to business became my initial North Star for developing industry award-level companies.

The beauty of the Interface approach to sustainability was that it reduced its negative impact on society and the environment and led to better products and increased profits. Their company has achieved a similar result in improving overall efficiency through a long-term focus on the higher initial investment in materials and methods that lead to more significant savings. The result was for me to adopt a holistic perspective of sustainability, which would not harm people and the planet.

A reflection on the content in the preceding chapters exhibits the collective positive impact on a manufacturing operation's internal and external stakeholders. The objective was to show the interconnectedness of the discipline areas necessary to run efficient and influential companies. Our communities are safer if we use processes and materials that have a net-zero or regenerative impact. If we break down employment barriers for those with different capabilities, we provide meaningful work for those currently unable to do so. The most beautiful outcome is that doing the right thing of excelling in the adoption of humanist commitments usually leads to best-in-class financial results. The increase in profits can be equitably shared and a portion reinvested in taking the company to another level of success.

HOW THE IRONMAN RELATES TO HUMANIST MANUFACTURING

I had watched the Ironman World Championship coverage on NBC for many years. It was a challenge I knew I needed to pursue at some point in my life. I accomplished this bucket list dream of completing the Ironman in 2013 in Louisville, Kentucky. I jumped into the Ohio River with over 2,500 of my new closest friends for a 2.4-mile swim that August morning. Next was a 112-mile bike ride through the rolling hills of Kentucky and the last leg of a 26.2-mile run through the streets of Louisville with temperatures reaching into the low 90 degrees Fahrenheit and high humidity. A highlight was passing the iconic Churchill Downs Racetrack. Fourteen hours and 17 minutes later, I earned the right to be called an Ironman. During the last few miles, I began to experience an intense high. I never slept that night, and this euphoric state lasted four days.

My pursuit of an Ironman coincided with the timeframe I was becoming immersed in the world of sustainability. A simple definition of sustainability is a triple bottom line of people (social), planet (environmental), and profit (financial). Becoming more sustainable usually requires a transition where companies move away from a primarily historical single bottom-line profit maximization focus. My thinking has since evolved to include the humanist manufacturing framework with additional characteristics.

The first similarity between an Ironman and becoming a humanist manufacturer is that we are often drawn to that in which we excel and are usually encouraged by others in our lives to do so. Many of us participated in multiple sports during our time in school. A select few individuals will emerge with strength in one discipline. Often, they begin to do that discipline year-round. For example, our son was a cross country and indoor and outdoor track athlete in his last two years in high school before doing the same at Michigan State University. As college students, we follow a similar path to find an academic major that resonates with us. Those who choose business often become more refined in accounting, finance, management, and marketing.

The second commonality is that those involved have little or no knowledge or experience in the other elements of an Ironman or applying humanist commitments. For example, participants who come to triathlons may excel in swimming, cycling, or running. However, hobbyists or competitive athletes must learn the other disciplines well enough to complete them before the various cutoff times. In addition, many companies have traditionally focused on a profit or financial bottom line and need to learn how to effectively implement the environmental and social areas. Therefore, these organizations would benefit from additional education and bringing in others with the requisite non-financial knowledge to support the transition to becoming a humanist manufacturing operation.

A third lesson is that both areas require a well-developed plan and hard work. Completing a physical activity in one day that covers 140.6 miles is impossible without following through with a well-developed training plan. It is also necessary to ingest the proper nutrition for the fuel needed to complete an Ironman. A company embracing the humanist manufacturing framework must also meet the appropriate action steps embedded in a culture that feeds and rewards those with an appetite for responsible business.

The good news is that many of us could complete an Ironman, and all of us can learn what it takes to lead an organization to become a humanist manufacturing operation. However, again, it will take the development of proper planning and a lot of time and effort. A year before my Ironman experience, I could barely swim a length of the pool. However, with lessons from a swim coach and practice, I was confident to take on and complete a 2.4-mile swim. Those needing to adopt the humanist commitments will likely need to find others to help them learn and adopt relevant humanist practices. The great news is that companies adopting practical humanist manufacturing commitments will become more profitable, leading to euphoria.

USING MATH TO SHOW THE IMPACT OF INCREMENTAL CHANGE

If we make small improvements, they collectively lead to a substantial impact. Thinking of this reminded me of something I saw on LinkedIn. I could not find it again, so I do not know who to give proper attribution or the exact equations, but it was something similar to:

$$1 \times 1 = 1$$
$$1 \times 1.01^{100} = 2.7$$
$$1 \times 1.01^{1000} = 20,959$$
$$1 \times 1.01^{10000} = 1.6e+43$$

It does an excellent job of showing the significant exponential impact resulting from a group of people making a little bit of improvement. Imagine the net result if we all became humanist manufacturing exemplars making substantial improvements to our plant operations. Are you ready to begin the work to be a humanist manufacturing exemplar? If so, let me know how I can help.

ACKNOWLEDGMENTS

I begin these remarks of appreciation to my wife, Kimberly. As with so many other accomplishments in my life, this book is not possible without her. I am always deeply appreciative that I have been blessed to have her as my life partner.

I am grateful to my parents, Joe and Linda Sprangel Sr, for teaching me a strong work ethic that taught me what it takes to get the job done. In addition, they were innovative in solving and accomplishing the task when an obstacle arose.

The final objective of a book ready for publication requires support from many people. I thank Christina Cain, Bruce Dorries, Jair Drooger, Jennifer Hancock, Jan Triplett, and Joanne Tritsch for reviewing the book content and providing valuable feedback that helped me refine further the insight I wanted to share with the reader.

We cannot see the seemingly obvious in our writing, so I appreciate the work of Arylynda Boyer and Linda Reviea for their editing prowess.

Michael Pirron, Founder & CEO of Impact Makers, has been integral in my understanding of the benefits of an organization becoming a Certified B Corp. His story of launching Impact Makers and ongoing support is invaluable.

The opportunity to occasionally bounce what I was pulling together off of Fred Keller, Founder & Chair of Cascade Engineering, was highly beneficial to my work. He has practiced what I offer in this book for nearly fifty years. What I have written parallels his work as a manufacturing exemplar in many ways.

I end with deep gratitude for Jackie Stavros. She was a faculty member in my DBA program and the person that introduced me to the work of Ray Anderson. Throughout my time as a student, she was a champion of my work to transition to an academic career. She has also positively impacted me as a person with her scholarly and practitioner work, as evidenced in this book. Jackie continues to support me long after graduation as a mentor and, more importantly, as a friend.

FURTHER RESOURCES

Humanist manufacturing focuses on the importance of integrated growth, moving toward self-actualization and transcendence for a production operation's internal and external stakeholders. The objective is to establish an environment focused on strengths that promote upward spirals toward optimal individual and organizational performance. The work occurs in a positive whole system setting that compels the natural human tendency of innate good to motivate the organization's members to generate positive environmental and social impacts. Ultimately, it has the additional beneficial outcome of all stakeholders of its ecosystem doing well financially. If you desire further resources, reach out to us at Emmanuel Strategic Sustainability to gain access to individual support or to discuss how we can collaborate to move your organization to higher levels of success.

Individuals interested in additional support for implementing all or part of the Humanist Manufacturing Framework should visit emmanuelstrategicsustainability.com. There you will find:

- *The Humanist Leadership Assessment.* The assessment will provide an evaluation of your current state as a humanist leader.
- *The Humanist Manufacturing Workbook* is a course that guides you through lessons in a self-paced format to move you from the concepts in the book to the full implementation of the humanist manufacturing framework.

An overview of the services provided by Emmanuel Strategic Sustainability (ESS) includes:

- Consulting support that improves business performance using a comprehensive, holistic perspective to collectively identify each stakeholder's opportunity to contribute positively to the desired business transformation.
- Training and reskilling to support the workforce in gaining the necessary current and future job skills to reach more extraordinary levels of the individual, team, and organizational potential.
- Coaching manufacturing leaders at all levels of the organization to develop a professional development strategy that will prepare them to lead their organization to transformational change.
- Fractional Chief Sustainability Officer support, where ESS is retained for a set number of hours per month to support the implementation of your sustainability initiatives. The focus is an improvement of your manufacturing operation's environmental, financial, and social impacts.

Those organizations that succeed in becoming humanist manufacturing operations will:

- Attract and retain talented employees seeking jobs that allow them to reach their full potential while working for a company with similar values to their own.
- Engage and empower all stakeholders that see organizations' significant gains with a transformational vision.
- Delight customers who feel good about engaging with a humanist company while being cared for by highly engaged employees.
- Lead to efficient and effective operations as the workforce commits to achieving the compelling "why" for the company's existence.

- Increase profitability where doing the right thing to improve your company's environmental and social impacts will also enhance financial results.
- Expand the positive impact within the walls of your organization, the greater community, and collectively the world.

NOTES

PREFACE

1. http://www.environmentandsociety.org/mml/ecology-commerce-declaration-sustainability
2. https://www.cascadeng.com/
3. http://www.environmentandsociety.org/mml/ecology-commerce-declaration-sustainability
4. https://www.worldbank.org/en/news/press-release/2020/10/07/covid-19-to-add-as-many-as-150-million-extreme-poor-by-2021
5. https://www.overshootday.org/2021-calculation/
6. https://www.globalcitizen.org/en/content/climate-change-is-connected-to-poverty/
7. https://www.nam.org/2-1-million-manufacturing-jobs-could-go-unfilled-by-2030-13743/
8. https://www2.deloitte.com/us/en/insights/industry/manufacturing/manufacturing-skills-gap-study.html
9. https://www.gallup.com/workplace/238085/state-american-workplace-report-2017.aspx
10. https://learn.dorieclark.com/courses/expert
11. https://www.barrywehmiller.com/
12. https://www.barrywehmiller.com/outreach/book
13. https://www.inc.com/marcel-schwantes/heres-a-top-10-list-of-the-worlds-best-ceos-but-they-lead-in-a-totally-unique-wa.html

INTRODUCTION

1. https://www.simplypsychology.org/maslow.html
2. https://online.hbs.edu/blog/post/what-is-the-triple-bottom-line
3. https://www.interface.com/US/en-US/sustainability/our-journey-en_US
4. https://www.interface.com/US/en-US/sustainability/our-journey-en_US
5. https://www.azquotes.com/author/22573-Ray_Anderson
6. https://www.linkedin.com/pulse/thriving-sustainably-mary-barra
7. https://www.barrywehmiller.com/story/leader/bob-chapman
8. https://www.patagonia.com/our-footprint/
9. https://www.forbes.com/sites/afdhelaziz/2019/08/05/the-power-of-purpose-how-virginie-helias-and-pg-are-making-sustainability-irresistible
10. https://progressivegrocer.com/pg-harnesses-innovation-accelerate-sustainable-change
11. https://www.renewableenergymagazine.com/hydrogen/h2-green-steel-initiative-aiums-to-produce-20210223
12. https://www.cascadeng.com/what-we-believe

1. A HUMANIST PERSPECTIVE

1. https://www.cbs.com/shows/undercover_boss/
2. https://www.goodreads.com/book/show/1336267.Strategic_Management
3. https://www.theatlantic.com/business/archive/2015/06/patagonia-labor-clothing-factory-exploitation/394658/
4. https://www.fairlabor.org/
5. https://www.verite.org/
6. https://americanhumanist.org/what-is-humanism/definition-of-humanism/
7. https://www.goodreads.com/en/book/show/461380.Humanist_Manifesto_2000
8. https://americanhumanistcenterforeducation.org/ten-commitments/
9. https://mcdonough.com/cradle-to-cradle/
10. http://interfaceinc.scene7.com/is/content/InterfaceInc/Interface/Americas/WebsiteContentAssets/Documents/Sustainability%2025yr%20Report/25yr%20Report%20Booklet%20Interface_MissionZeroCel.pdf
11. https://www.worldbank.org/en/news/press-release/2020/10/07/covid-19-to-add-as-many-as-150-million-extreme-poor-by-2021
12. https://hbr.org/2018/11/business-does-not-need-the-humanities-but-humans-do
13. https://www.businessexpertpress.com/books/applied-humanism-how-to-create-more-effective-and-ethical-businesses/

2. KNOWING THYSELF

1. https://www.huffpost.com/entry/ubuntu-applying-african-p_b_1243904
2. https://positiveorgs.bus.umich.edu/summaries/leadership/
3. https://www.apa.org/monitor/oct05/mirror
4. https://www.ihhp.com/meaning-of-emotional-intelligence/
5. https://hbr.org/2017/02/emotional-intelligence-has-12-elements-which-do-you-need-to-work-on
6. https://www.6seconds.org/2019/02/13/amadori-case-engagement-emotional-intelligence/
7. https://www.cio.com/article/219940/thriving-in-a-world-of-knowledge-half-life.html
8. https://www.triplepundit.com/story/2015/5-steps-expanding-your-expertise-become-better-leader/30576
9. https://www.interface.com/US/en-US/sustainability/our-history-en_US
10. https://encore.org/purpose-prize/ray-anderson/
11. https://www.iecl.com/why-coaching-why-now

3. WHY, VISION, MISSION, AND VALUES

1. https://simonsinek.com/product/start-with-why/
2. https://www.ted.com/talks/simon_sinek_how_great_leaders_inspire_action
3. https://www.kotterinc.com/book/leading-change/
4. https://news.gallup.com/businessjournal/181175/factory-workers-don-care-company-mission.aspx
5. https://hbr.org/2002/07/make-your-values-mean-something

6. https://www.britannica.com/event/Enron-scandal
7. https://time.com/3423136/tylenol-deaths-1982/
8. https://www.interface.com/US/en-US/sustainability/our-history-en_US
9. https://www.nytimes.com/2002/03/23/your-money/IHT-tylenol-made-a-hero-of-johnson-johnson-the-recall-that-started.html
10. https://cascadeng.com/our-culture

4. KNOWING THY EXECUTIVE TEAM

1. https://www.gallup.com/cliftonstrengths/en/253832/cliftonstrengths-for-teams.aspx
2. https://store.gallup.com/p/en-us/10003/cliftonstrengths-34
3. https://www.thinkherrmann.com/hubfs/Herrmann_Inclusive_Leadership_Playbook.pdf
4. https://www.herrmann-europe.com/en/our-tools-2/the-team-profile
5. https://www.predictiveindex.com/assessments/cognitive-assessment/
6. https://www.predictiveindex.com/assessments/job-assessment/
7. https://www.predictiveindex.com/assessments/behavioral-assessment/

PHASE 3 OVERVIEW

1. https://www.indeed.com/career-advice/career-development/business-operating-system

5. THE BUSINESS OPERATING SYSTEM

1. Honeyman, R. (2014). The B Corp Handbook: How to Use Business as a Force for Good. San Francisco: Berrett-Koehler Publishers, Inc.
2. https://www.bcorporation.net/en-us/about-b-corps/legal-requirements
3. https://www.bcorporation.net/en-us/programs-and-tools/b-impact-assessment
4. https://kb.bimpactassessment.net/support/solutions/articles/43000574683-impact-areas-governance-workers-community-environment-and-customers
5. https://www.bcorporation.net/en-us/find-a-b-corp
6. https://sdgs.un.org/goals
7. https://theleanway.net/The-8-Wastes-of-Lean
8. https://flevy.com/blog/14-principles-of-lean-toyota-production-system-tps/
9. https://mitpress.mit.edu/books/out-crisis

6. PRODUCT DESIGN

1. https://www.plasticstoday.com/business/design-world-war-ii-plastics-and-npe
2. https://aclima.eus/what-will-it-take-to-redesign-a-hyper-disposable-world/
3. https://epea.com/en/
4. https://researchoutreach.org/articles/cradle-cradle-principles-change-products-designed
5. https://epea.com/en/services

6. https://sustainabilityguide.eu/methods/cradle-to-cradle/
7. https://epea.com/en/about-us/cradle-to-cradle
8. https://mcdonough.com/cradle-to-cradle/
9. https://www.ted.com/talks/william_mcdonough_cradle_to_cradle_design
10. https://biomimicry.org/janine-benyus/
11. https://www.industryweek.com/innovation/media-gallery/21964966/nature-rules-10-biomimicry-projects-that-are-changing-product-design
12. https://www.sculpteo.com/blog/2018/07/11/nature-inspired-3d-printing-introducing-biomimicry/
13. https://cets-eu.be/2020/05/08/the-importance-of-surface-treatment/
14. https://www.scribd.com/document/399887020/Surface-Engg
15. https://surfaceengineering.com/
16. https://www.sdsmt.edu/SERC/

7. MATERIALS SELECTION

1. https://static1.squarespace.com/static/585c3439be65942f022bbf9b/t/5ef223cbf5d8e025b9d2fee/1592927193457/RethinkX+Humanity+Report.pdf
2. https://www.linkedin.com/pulse/what-lightweighting-why-do-we-need-avi-reichental-/
3. https://www.epa.gov/newsreleases/us-dot-and-epa-put-safety-and-american-families-first-final-rule-fuel-economy-standards
4. https://www.lucintel.com/lucintelBriefFile/201211-Developments%20in%20Global%20Composites%20Industy-Lucintel-12-15-2020.pdf
5. https://www.graphenea.com/pages/graphene
6. https://www.sciencedaily.com/releases/2020/06/200603122949.htm
7. https://www.prnewswire.com/news-releases/navigate-the-emerging-graphene-market-at-graphene-and-2d-materials-europe-2020-301001967.html
8. https://singularityhub.com/2018/08/05/beyond-graphene-the-promise-of-2d-materials/
9. https://3dprintingindustry.com/news/cfam-researchers-investigate-inkjet-printed-graphene-for-new-generation-optoelectronic-devices-178594/
10. https://medium.com/advanced-composite-training/what-is-a-composite-174e16c60cc2
11. https://www.advancedcomposites.com/composites-manufacturing/frequently-asked-questions/
12. https://www.asminternational.org/documents/10192/22833166/05287G_Sample_BuyNow.pdf
13. https://www.textileworld.com/textile-world/features/2017/03/advanced-composite-materials-and-manufacturing-in-vehicles-wind-and-compressed-gas-storage/
14. https://iacmi.org/
15. https://technology.nasa.gov/

8. PROCESSES

1. https://static1.squarespace.com/static/585c3439be65942f022bbf9b/t/5ef223cbf
f5d8e025b9d2fee/1592927193457/RethinkX+Humanity+Report.pdf
2. https://www.pcmag.com/news/3d-printing-what-you-need-to-know
3. https://www.mckinsey.com/business-functions/operations/our-insights/additive-manufacturing-a-long-term-game-changer-for-manufacturers
4. https://www.mckinsey.com/industries/metals-and-mining/our-insights/how-3d-printing-will-transform-the-metals-industry
5. https://www.plasticsmachinerymagazine.com/additive-manufacturing/article/13000759
6. https://www.researchgate.net/publication/315640918_Decentralization_and_Localization_of_Production_The_Organizational_and_Economic_Consequences_of_Additive_Manufacturing_3D_Printing
7. https://www2.deloitte.com/us/en/insights/focus/internet-of-things/technical-primer.html
8. https://www.mckinsey.com/business-functions/operations/our-insights/industrial-iot-generates-real-value-if-businesses-overcome-six-myths
9. https://www.saviantconsulting.com/blog/3-industrial-iot-implementations-manufacturing.aspx
10. https://ifr.org/ifr-press-releases/news/robot-density-rises-globally
11. https://www.pwc.com/us/en/industries/industrial-products/library/industrial-robot-ready.html
12. https://www.industryweek.com/technology-and-iiot/article/21144713/do-robots-need-a-sense-of-touch
13. https://www.capgemini.com/consulting-de/wp-content/uploads/sites/32/2017/08/robotic-process-automation-study.pdf
14. https://www.mckinsey.com/~/media/McKinsey/Business%20Functions/Operations/Our%20Insights/Mature%20quality%20systems/2014062_mature_quality_systems.pdf
15. https://www.heavy.ai/technical-glossary/embedded-systems
16. https://metrology.news/new-report-predicts-manufacturing-transformation-by-2030/
17. https://www.kinematics.com/about/newsletterarticlesainairbus.php
18. https://link.springer.com/content/pdf/10.1007%2F978-981-10-5192-0_16-1.pdf

9. SUSTAINABLE OPERATIONS

1. https://www.harbec.com/wp-content/uploads/2019/03/Harbec-Case-Study.pdf
2. https://www.iso.org/standard/62085.html
3. https://www.iso.org/iso-14001-environmental-management.html
4. https://www.iso.org/standard/69426.html
5. https://www.harbec.com/sustainable-manufacturing/
6. https://www.usgbc.org/leed
7. https://delval.edu/community-members/spark-bowl/michael-araten
8. https://www.youtube.com/watch?v=YUVQkP-0xUI
9. https://www.rodongroup.com/blog/a-green-and-sustainable-factory-at-the-rodon-group

10. https://pre-sustainability.com/legacy/download/EI99_Manual.pdf
11. https://www.businesswire.com/news/home/20210604005078/en/Trane-Technologies-Appoints-Dave-Regnery-as-Chief-Executive-Officer-Mike-Lamach-to-Serve-as-Executive-Chair-Through-Transition
12. https://www.tranetechnologies.com/en/index/sustainability.html
13. https://www.terrapinbrightgreen.com/blog/2018/02/factory-as-a-forest/
14. https://capitalinstitute.org/8-principles-regenerative-economy/
15. https://www.ncbi.nlm.nih.gov/pmc/articles/PMC7498239/

10. PUTTING EMPLOYEES FIRST

1. https://www.inc.com/oscar-raymundo/richard-branson-companies-should-put-employees-first.html
2. https://www.gallup.com/workplace/285818/state-american-workplace-report.aspx
3. https://fortune.com/best-companies/
4. https://www.mckinsey.com/business-functions/organization/our-insights/the-boss-factor-making-the-world-a-better-place-through-workplace-relationships
5. https://www.acra.com.au/how-to-boost-employee-morale-in-a-factory-setting/
6. https://www.forbes.com/sites/rebeccaskilbeck/2019/02/12/six-strategies-to-maintain-employee-motivation
7. https://workplaceinsight.net/neuroscience-can-functions-management-tool-personal-development/
8. https://neurochangesolutions.com/use-it-or-lose-it/
9. https://www.octanner.com/global-culture-report.html
10. https://www.octanner.com/insights/articles/2020/1/9/_10_employee_recogni.html
11. In Google, use the search term "Designing and Managing Incentive Compensation Programs" to access the article.
12. https://www.industryweek.com/talent/article/22028340/inspiring-the-next-generation-of-manufacturing-employees

11. BUILDING THRIVING COMMUNITIES

1. https://nestingdolls.co/blogs/posts/history-nesting-dolls
2. https://www.themanufacturinginstitute.org/research/2018-deloitte-and-the-manufacturing-institute-skills-gap-and-future-of-work-study/
3. https://www.thomasnet.com/insights/must-read-advice-from-6-successful-women-in-industry-q-a/
4. https://www.womeninmanufacturing.org/
5. https://www.mckinsey.com/featured-insights/diversity-and-inclusion/women-in-the-workplace
6. https://sperocareerscanada.ca/admbusinesscase/
7. https://lexingtonservices.com/career-paths-for-people-with-autism/
8. https://lhblind.org/
9. https://www.pvcc.edu/community-business/network2work
10. https://www.greyston.org/open-hiring
11. https://www.insider.com/guides/style/b-corp-retail-companies

12. https://dvsv3.com/
13. https://www.youtube.com/watch?v=EpuhjKXlYvE
14. https://www.cascadeng.com/what-we-believe
15. https://bcorporation.net/
16. https://www.benice.org/
17. https://tcf.org/content/report/revitalizing-americas-manufacturing-communities/

12. DEVELOPING THE COMPANY STRATEGY

1. https://conversationsworthhaving.today/
2. Stavros, J., Cooperrider, D. & Kelley, D. (2007). SOAR: A new approach to strategic planning, The Change Handbook: The Definitive Resource on Today's Best Methods for Engaging Whole Systems (eds. Holman, P., Devane, T. & Cady, S.) (2nd ed.), San Francisco: Berrett-Koehler Publishers, Inc. www.soar-strategy.com
3. https://www.davidcooperrider.com/ai-process/
4. Holman, P., Devane, T., & Cady, S. (2007). The Change Handbook. San Francisco: Berrett-Koehler Publishers, Inc. https://www.bkconnection.com/home/books/fast-fundamentals-whitepapers/the-change-handbook-chapters
5. Cooperrider, D. & Srivastva, S. (1987). Appreciative inquiry in organizational life, Research in Organizational Change and Development, 1, (ed. Woodman, R. and Pasmore, W.), 129-169, Greenwich, CT: JAI Press. https://www.oio.nl/wp-content/uploads/APPRECIATIVE_INQUIRY_IN_Orgnizational_life.pdf
6. www.soar-strategy.com
7. de Kluyver, C. & Pearce, J. (2006). Strategy: A View from the Top, Upper Saddle River, NJ: Prentice Hall. https://www.amazon.com/Strategy-View-Cornelis-Kluyver/dp/0132145626
8. www.soar-strategy.com
9. www.soar-strategy.com
10. www.soar-strategy.com
11. Isern, J. & Pung, J. (2007). Driving radical change. The McKinsey Quarterly. 4. https://www.mckinsey.com/business-functions/people-and-organizational-performance/our-insights/driving-radical-change
12. http://www.thepeoplehistory.com/vacuum.html
13. https://www.gm.com/electric-vehicles.html
14. https://www.npr.org/2016/08/22/490932307/aging-and-unstable-the-nations-electrical-grid-is-the-weakest-link
15. https://www.automotiveworld.com/articles/risky-business-the-hidden-costs-of-ev-battery-raw-materials/
16. https://www.theguardian.com/sustainable-business/2017/aug/10/electric-cars-big-battery-waste-problem-lithium-recycling

13. THE IMPORTANCE OF TACTICAL PLANS

1. https://www.nist.gov/baldrige/publications/baldrige-excellence-framework

14. THE CHANGE PROCESS

1. https://www.kotterinc.com/8-steps-e-book-download/
2. Presentation at the Malcolm Baldrige 2022 Quest for Exellence Conference

CONCLUSION

1. https://www.youtube.com/watch?v=QvU35PbKwOk

ABOUT THE AUTHOR

Joe Sprangel, DBA, is an associate professor of business at Mary Baldwin University. He is also the founder and principal consultant of Emmanuel Strategic Sustainability. He blends his academic and industry backgrounds to redefine the role of manufacturing—to an industry that efficiently and effectively balances environmental, financial, and social success that leads to more inclusive and sustainable local economies for all community members.

He is active in thought leadership, where manufacturing plays a more substantial role as an integral element of a thriving community. His work explores opportunities to engage members of society who have not generally been considered employable. These individuals can be on the autism spectrum, persons with perceived disabilities, minorities, returning citizens, veterans, and women. The manufacturing industry has opportunities that can allow each citizen of the world to meet, at a minimum, their needs for just and healthy lives—one where manufacturing exists for a higher purpose far beyond making a profit for shareholders.

He made the transition to higher education after 28 years of industry experience. His previous work included machine build and repair, machine design, manufacturing engineering, and plant and engineering management. The work experience led to his interest in developing courses and programs emphasizing learning while doing assignments and projects that replicate the work done in the industry.

Sprangel earned a Doctor of Business Administration degree from Lawrence Technological University. He also holds Master of Business Administration degrees from Spring Arbor University, a Bachelor of Business Administration from Eastern Michigan University, and an Associate Degree in Mechanical Engineering Technology.